The Nostalgia Quiz Book #3

The Nostalgia Quiz Book #3

MARTIN A. GROSS

BONANZA BOOKS · NEW YORK

INTRODUCTION

In addition to the more than 140 quizzes with over 1,400 questions, there are two special features in this, the third in *The Nostalgia Quiz Book* series.

The first feature is a collection of 10 crossword puzzles with nostalgic clues. Since the crossword puzzle is celebrating its fiftieth anniversary as I compile this quiz book, it's an especially fitting trivia testing tool. You'll find these "Quiz-Word" puzzles scattered throughout the book. Their solutions are in the back, along with the answers to all the other quizzes. My special thanks to Dave Shulman, the eminent cryptologist and puzzle expert, for his assistance in constructing these "Quiz-Word" puzzles.

The second feature is a "Semi-Official Nostalgia Diary." It's a day-by-day quiz recalling an event of the past that fell on that particular day. You'll find the diary at the end of the quiz section, with the answers at the end of the answer section.

Lots of memory testing here, so sharpen your pencil and start recalling!

1. CASTING CALL

† † † † †

Match the cast with the movie.

1. *Slightly Dangerous*
2. *Blondie Knows Best*
3. *Manhattan Melodrama*
4. *Deep Valley*
5. *Men Are Not Gods*
6. *The Fireball*
7. *Never Say Die*
8. *Mississippi*
9. *First Love*
10. *No Man of Her Own*

a) Myrna Loy, Leo Carillo, Mickey Rooney

b) Miriam Hopkins, Gertrude Lawrence, Rex Harrison

c) Bing Crosby, W.C. Fields, Joan Bennett

d) Martha Raye, Bob Hope, Andy Devine, Gale Sondergaard

e) Penny Singleton, Arthur Lake, Larry Simms, Marjorie Kent

f) Lana Turner, Robert Walker, Walter Brennan, Dame May Whitty, Eugene Pallette

g) Ida Lupino, Dane Clark, Wayne Morris, Fay Bainter, Henry Hull

h) Mickey Rooney, Pat O'Brien, Beverly Taylor, Marilyn Monroe, Milburn Stone

i) Clark Gable, Carole Lombard, Dorothy Mackaill, Grant Mitchell

j) Deanna Durbin, Robert Stack, Helen Parrish

† † †

7

2. YOU'RE A GOOD GROUP

Match the leader and the musical group.

1. Horace Heidt   a) City Slickers
2. Bill Haley   b) Gramercy Five
3. Kid Ory   c) Comets
4. Artie Shaw   d) Musical Knights
5. Spike Jones   e) Red Hot Peppers
6. Larry Funk   f) Commanders
7. Irving Aaronson   g) Band of a Thousand Melodies
8. Jelly Roll Morton   h) Original Creole Jazz Band

✝ ✝ ✝

3. LIFETIME STARS

✝ ✝ ✝ ✝ ✝

1. He first appeared in 1916 in *The Primitive Strain*, and was last seen in 1956 in *The Ambassador's Daughter*. In between he was in *Rasputin and the Empress, Diamond Jim, Come and Get It, The Toast of New York, You Can't Take It With You, Mr. Smith Goes to Washington, Lillian Russell, Meet John Doe, Mrs. Parkington, Weekend at the Waldorf, Dear Ruth* and *The Hucksters*.

2. In 1922 he was in *Silver Wings*. In 1969 he was in *Butch Cassidy and the Sundance Kid*. He was also in *Miracle on 34th Street, Call Northside 777, Call Me Madam, The Robe, How to Marry a Millionaire, A Star is Born* and *The Music Man*.

3. He was first seen in *The Great Gatsby*, 1926, and last in 1955's *Bowery to Bagdad*. In between he was in *Flying Down to Rio, Gay Divorcee, Limehouse Blues, Diamond Jim, Top Hat, Sev-*

en Keys to Baldpate, Swing Time, Shall We Dance, The Boys from Syracuse, The Lady Eve and Sullivan's Travels.

4. He was in the short, Let 'Er Go, 1920, and in Fortunes of Captain Blood, 1950. He was also in Vanity Fair, Cavalcade, The Lost Patrol, Limehouse Blues, A Tale of Two Cities, Tin Pan Alley, Dr. Jekyll and Mr. Hyde, The Lodger, National Velvet and Cluny Brown.

5. He was in Something Always Happens, 1928, and in Arriverderci, Baby, 1966. He was also in The Benson Murder Case, Tarzan, Lives of a Bengal Lancer, The Crusades, Clive of India, The Princess Comes Across, My Man Godfrey, Winterset, You Can't Take It With You, Destry Rides Again, And Then There Were None.

6. He was first seen in Birth of a Nation, 1915, and last in 1954's Apache. He was also in Orphans of the Storm, White Shadows of the South Seas, Come On, Marines, G-Men, Souls at Sea, Juarez, The Palm Beach Story, Edge of Darkness and Life with Father.

7. His first movie was Salute (1929): His last, Alias Jesse James (1959). In between he was in It Happened One Night, The Informer, Dead End, Gone With The Wind, The Grapes of Wrath, The Long Voyage Home, Sergeant York, The Maltese Falcon, The Fugitive, Fort Apache, The Quiet Man and The Long Grey Line.

8. His first picture was Each Pearl a Tear, 1916; his last Man in The Shadow, 1957. He also appeared in Penrod and Sam, All Quiet on the Western Front, Tom Brown of Culver and The Leather Pushers.

9. In 1921 he was in The Sin Flood; in 1949, the Fountainhead. He was also in Souls for Sale, The Vanishing American, Seven Keys to Baldpate, Cimarron and The Whistler.

10. She debuted in The Nightingale, 1914, and exited after Johnny Trouble, 1957. She was also in Kiss of Hate, Rasputin and The Empress, None but the Lonely Heart, The Spiral Staircase, The Farmer's Daughter, Moss Rose, The Paradine Case, Portrait of Jennie, The Midnight Kiss, Pinky and It's a Big Country.

11. She debuted in 1912's *The New York Hat* and was last seen in 1964's *The Chalk Garden*. She was also in *Judith of Bethulia, Hearts of the World, Orphans of the Storm, Our Hearts Were Young and Gay, Centennial Summer,* and *The Cardinal.*

    a) Ethel Barrymore
    b) Percy Helton
    c) Ben Alexander
    d) Ward Bond
    e) Billy Bevan
    f) Dorothy Gish
    g) Richard Dix
    h) Eric Blore
    i) Monte Blue
    j) Mischa Auer
    k) Edward Arnold

† † †

4. MOSTLY FORGOTTEN

† † † † †

1. What was the New Deal's NYA?

* * *

2. What was *The Stocking Parade?*

* * *

3. What were Higgins boats?

* * *

4. What were Fleetwoods?

5. Who were Crossley and Hooper?

* * *

6. What were Strato-Pens?

7. What was the "Ferdinand Magellan"?

* * *

8. Who wanted to set up a California government of communes under the slogan "I Produce, I Defend"?

* * *

9. Who discovered the neutron?

* * *

10. What did Horton's make?

† † †

5. SCORECARD MONICKERS

† † † † †

Match the name and the nickname.

1. Nat Clifton		**a)** Automatic Jack
2. Jack Manders		**b)** Sweetwater
3. Ralph Weiland		**c)** The Toe
4. Henri Richard		**d)** Deacon Dan
5. Archie Moore		**e)** Night Train
6. Harry Greb		**f)** Big Daddy
7. Gene Lipscomb		**g)** The Pittsburgh Windmill
8. Dick Lane		**h)** The Mongoose
9. Dan Towler		**i)** Pocket Rocket
10. Lou Groza		**j)** Cooney

† † †

Quiz-Word No. 1

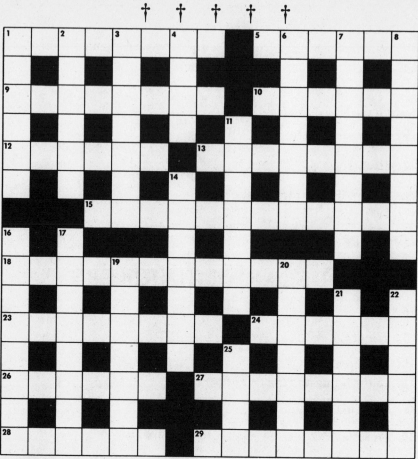

ACROSS
1. Ballet movie (3, 5).
5. *Nothing* ——— (6).
9. Maugham (8).
10. ——— *Wore Tights* (6).
12. A Hays Office no-no theme (6).
13. Bugs Bunny, among others (3, 5).
15. Singer of "My Mother's Eyes" (6, 6).
18. Movie with Doris Day and Ray Bolger (5, 2, 5).
23. Gable role (8).
24. Seventh Cavalry mission (6).
26. Riggers and drillers (6).
27. Sports footwear or lurkers (8).
28. Of the Marx brothers, Chico was the ——— (6).
29. Excused (8).

DOWN
1. *All the King's Men* producer-director (6).
2. Walt's elephant and family (6).
3. Female lead (7).
4. *East of* ——— (4).
6. Ronald Colman's ——— *Life* (1, 6).
7. Practice (8).
8. Without a go-between (8).
11. Patton's rank, Keaton's movie (7).
14. Yul (7).
16. Mr. Holmes, I presume? (8).
17. Silent screen star Wesley Barry, for instance (8).
19. Pays attention (7).
20. Locale of *The Quiet Man* (7).
21. The Silver ——— (6).
22. Photographed (6).
25. ——— *Karenina* (4).

12

6. COME-AND-GONE ATTRACTIONS

† † † † †

Match the film and the stars.

1. *Escape*
2. *Exclusive*
3. *First Comes Courage*
4. *Going Places*
5. *The Great Man Votes*
6. *Hello, Frisco, Hello*
7. *Hired Wife*
8. *Diamond Jim*
9. *Diary of a Chambermaid*
10. *Diplomatic Courier*

a) Merle Oberon, Brian Aherne, Carl Esmond

b) John Barrymore, Peter Holden, Virginia Weidler

c) Rosalind Russell, Brian Aherne, Virginia Bruce

d) Paulette Goddard, Burgess Meredith, Hurd Hatfield

e) Edward Arnold, Jean Arthur, Binnie Barnes

f) Norma Shearer, Robert Taylor, Conrad Veidt

g) Fred MacMurray, Frances Farmer, Lloyd Nolan

h) Dick Powell, Anita Louise, Allen Jenkins, Ronald Reagan

i) Alice Faye, John Payne, Jack Oakie, Lynn Bari

j) Henry Hathaway, Tyrone Power, Patricia Neal

† † †

7. WARTIME DRAMA

† † † † †

During World War II, who

1. Was a colonel in the Air Force?
2. Commanded a destroyer at Normandy?
3. Served in the South Pacific?
4. Shot down seven Japanese planes?
5. Flew 50 missions as a tailgunner?

a) Wayne Morris
b) Henry Fonda
c) Sabu
d) Jimmy Stewart
e) Robert Montgomery

† † †

8. NOMS DE SPORT

† † † † †

Match the nickname and the man.

1. Norm Van Brocklin	a) The Galloping Ghost
2. Albie Booth	b) The Flying Parson
3. Alan Ameche	c) Champagne Tony
4. Charlie Justice	d) The Dutchman
5. John McNally	e) The Horse
6. George Woolf	f) Choo Choo
7. Eddie LeBaron	g) The Little General
8. Tony Lema	h) Johnny Blood
9. Red Grange	i) The Mighty Atom
10. Gil Dodds	j) The Iceman

9. YOU AUTO KNOW

† † † † †

Match the car model with the manufacturer.

1. Rockne Six	a)	General Motors
2. Airflow	b)	Studebaker
3. Superior	c)	Chevrolet
4. Speedabout	d)	Stutz
5. Erskine	e)	Kaiser-Frazier
6. Terraplane	f)	Essex
7. Bantam Club	g)	Hudson
8. Viking	h)	Chrysler
9. Bearcat	i)	American Austin
10. Henry J.		

† † †

10. COMIC CHARACTERS

† † † † †

1. Who runs the restaurant where Wimpy eats his hamburgers?

* * *

2. Whom did Walt Wallet ("Gasoline Alley") marry?

* * *

3. What's the name of Little Iodine's father?

15

4. Who owned Spare Ribs?

* * *

5. What's the first name of Snuffy Smith's wife?

* * *

6. What does the Inspector in "The Katzenjammer Kids" do for a living?

* * *

7. Where do you find J.P. McKee?

* * *

8. What is Uncle Elby's dog's name?

* * *

9. What's the name of Annie Rooney's dog?

* * *

10. What's the name of the cat in "Smokey Stover"?

* * *

11. Where did you find Tagalong?

† † †

11. HOLLYWOOD TRAGEDIES #1

† † † † †

1. Who was the 41-year-old Western actor who poisoned himself in 1931, in Chihuahua, Mexico? He had been divorced from Edythe Sterling and Louise Lorraine.

* * *

2. Who was the 36-year-old actor who died from a drug overdose in 1968? He had been nominated for Best Supporting Actor Oscar for his performance in *Twilight of Honor.*

* * *

3. Who was the 30-year-old actor who shot himself in 1937? He was married to Ann Nagel, and had appeared in *A Midsummer Night's Dream, Captain Blood* and *China Clipper.*

* * *

4. Who was the 39-year-old actress who died from a drug overdose in 1971? She had been divorced from Vic Damone.

* * *

5. Who was the fabulously successful comic who found all doors closed to him after a sensational trial? Using the pseudonym of William Goodrich, he did direct a few movies.

* * *

6. Who was the 33-year-old killed when his RCAF plane crashed? He had debuted in *Varsity* in 1928 and had appeared in *An American Tragedy, Great Expectations* and *Nana,* among other films.

* * *

7. Who was the 22-year-old actress (*The Ladies' Man*), daughter of a well-known columnist, who was murdered in 1963?

* * *

8. Who was the 31-year-old actress (*The Prisoner of Zenda*) who died in 1925 as the result of stringent dieting?

* * *

9. Who was the 29-year-old actress who committed suicide in 1948? She had appeared in *A Star is Born, Topper Returns, My Gal Sal,* and *Four Jills in a Jeep.*

10. Who was "The Biograph Girl" who committed suicide in 1938 by eating ant paste?

12. SCREENING ROOM

✝   ✝   ✝   ✝   ✝

Match the movie and the actors.

1. *The Lost Moment*
2. *All the Fine Young Cannibals*
3. *Anything Can Happen*
4. *Barabbas*
5. *Beach Party*
6. *The Big Gamble*
7. *Branded*
8. *Doll Face*
9. *The Earl of Chicago*
10. *Embraceable You*

a) Mona Freeman, Charles Bickford, Alan Ladd

b) Frankie Avalon, Annette Funicello

c) Jose Ferrer, Kim Hunter, Kurt Kaznar

d) Robert Cummings, Susan Hayward, Agnes Moorehead

e) Dane Clark, Geraldine Brooks, S.Z. Sakall

f) Vivian Blaine, Dennis O'Keefe, Perry Como

g) Anthony Quinn, Jack Palance, Arthur Kennedy

h) Natalie Wood, George Hamilton, Susan Kohner

i) Stephen Boyd, Juliette Greco, David Wayne

j) Robert Montgomery, Edward Arnold, Reginald Owen

✝   ✝   ✝

13. COMMEMORATIVES

1. Who was William J. Burns?

       *   *   *

2. Whose arrangements did Benny Goodman feature at the Palomar Ballroom, Los Angeles, August 21, 1935?

       *   *   *

3. Who drove his Blue Bird car at 272.1 mph?

       *   *   *

4. Who was the author who landed a 468-lb. marlin without harness in the early 30s?

       *   *   *

5. What was the collective name of Republic, National, Inland, Bethlehem and Youngstown Sheet and Tube?

       *   *   *

6. Lt. Commander J. J. Hughes commanded: a) the "Panay"; b) the "Oklahoma" or c) the "Hornet"?

       *   *   *

7. Who took you to "The Meridian room in the Hotel Park Plaza, to be entertained by the music of Ramon Raquello and his orchestra"?

       *   *   *

8. Who was the young American, son of our Ambassador, who interviewed survivors of the U-Boat-attacked SS "Athenia" in 1939?

9. Who was R. Douglas Stuart, Jr.?

* * *

10. What was Prof. Charles Dawes of Harvard deriding in 1939 when he said, "It must take place in a semi-darkened room and it demands constant attention."?

14. COLLEGE MEN

† † † † †

Match the college and the man.

1. Frank Sinkwich		a) Notre Dame
2. Red Blaik		b) UCLA
3. Bob Zastrow		c) Washington & Jefferson
4. Amos Alonzo Stagg		d) Kansas
5. George Mikan		e) Wisconsin
6. Knute Rockne		f) Louisiana State
7. Frankie Baumholtz		g) Chicago
8. Dutch Meyer		h) Stanford
9. Lynn Chadnois		i) Michigan State
10. Fielding Yost		j) Ohio University
11. Hank Luisetti		k) DePaul
12. Lou Little		l) Navy
13. George Connor		m) Georgia
14. Jay Berwanger		n) Army
15. Y. A. Tittle		o) Texas Christian
16. Glenn Cunningham		p) Michigan

17. Elroy Hirsch   q) Columbia

18. Earl Neale

19. Bob Waterfield

20. Paul Horning

15. MASONRY

† † † † †

Complete the Perry Mason novel title.

The Case of the . . .

1. Velvet	a) Face
2. Curious	b) Legs
3. Howling	c) Cat
4. Caretaker's	d) Parrot
5. Sleepwalker's	e) Eye
6. Sulky	f) Bones
7. Lucky	g) Niece
8. Counterfeit	h) Hook
9. Stuttering	i) Claws
10. Lame	j) Bishop
11. Substitute	k) Girl
12. Rolling	l) Dowager
13. Dangerous	m) Bride
14. Shoplifter's	n) Canary
15. Baited	o) Dog
16. Perjured	p) Show

16. MOVIE MISCELLANY

† † † † †

1.   The hero was Glenn Ford; who was the heroine in John Farrow's *Plunder of the Sun?*

*   *   *

2.   Who played the secretary in *Parachute Jumper* whom Leo Carillo was after?

*   *   *

3.   What do Claire Trevor, Blanche Yurka and Shelley Winters have in common?

*   *   *

4.   What do Sylvia Sidney, Peggy Cummins, Dorothy Provine and Faye Dunaway have in common?

*   *   *

5.   In what film did Cecil B. De Mille use a rubber squid?

*   *   *

6.   With what actor were all these women associated: Lily Damita, Betty Hamsen, Peggy Satterlee, and Nora Eddington?

*   *   *

7.   Who composed the scores for *King of Kings, Quo Vadis, Spellbound,* and *El Cid?*

*   *   *

8.   Who was Dorothy Dale?

9. Al "Fuzzy" St. John was which comic's nephew?

*   *   *

10. What was Alma Kruger's role in the "Dr. Kildare" films?

†   †   †

17. LONG TIME WE SEE

†   †   †   †   †

1. In 1916 he was in *Oliver Twist,* and in 1967 in *In Cold Blood.* And in between he was in *Male and Female, The Virginian, Arrowsmith, Love Finds Andy Hardy, Northwest Trail, The Texas Kid, Six-Gun Gospel* and *Requiem for a Gunfighter.*
2. He ranged from *The Roman* (1908) to *Bullet Scars* (1942). And he also was in *Sea Wolf, The Little American, The Big Parade, Freckles, Abraham Lincoln, Dirigible, The Miracle Man, Last of the Mohicans, Whom the Gods Destroy* and *One Foot in Heaven.*
3. In 1920 he was in *49 East* and in 1966, *Batman.* He also was seen in *The Iron Trail,* the "Leather Pusher" series, *Of Human Bondage, The Patrol, Bulldog Drummond's Bride, Captains of the Clouds, The Macomber Affair, Mr. Blandings Builds His Dream House* and *Cat Ballou.*
4. She debuted in *Rose of the Rancho,* 1914, and exited in *Mary Poppins,* 1964. In between she was featured in *Tom Sawyer, Back Street, Jennie Gerhardt, Design for Living, The Singing Marine, Jesse James, The Rains Came, Gone With the Wind, The Grapes of Wrath, Chad Hanna, Tender Comrade, The Time of Your Life, Caged* and *The Last Hurrah.*
5. She was in *Intolerance,* 1915, and *Whirlpool,* 1950. She was also in *Bleak House, Dinner at Eight, Peter Ibbetson, Little Lord Fauntleroy, Stage Door, Susan and God, Monsieur Beaucaire* and *Rope.*

23

6. He starred in the "Ambrose-Walrus" series of 1913 and was also in 1966's *A Big Hand for the Little Lady.* He appeared in *Anna Christie, Desire, Souls for Sale, The Phantom of the Opera, The Gold Rush, Tillie's Punctured Romance, Modern Times, The Great Dictator* and *Knickerbocker Holiday.*

7. He was in 1924's *Second Youth* and in 1957's *Beau James.* He also appeared in *Why Leave Home?, Back Street, Rain, A Tale of Two Cities, Mr. Deeds Goes to Town, Love is News, Bringing Up Baby, Zaza, Manpower, Star Spangled Rhythm, The Boy With Green Hair* and *The Inspector General.*

8. In 1911 he was in *Last Year.* In 1966 he was in *The Ghost in the Invisible Bikini.* He was also in *Graustark, Romeo and Juliet, Ben Hur, Wilson* and *David and Bathsheba.*

9. She was in *One Night Stand* (1915) and *Stork Club* (1945). She also was in *Foolish Wives, Souls for Sale, The Unholy Three, While the City Sleeps, Doctor X, Sons of the Desert, Prison Farm* and *Nancy Drew, Detective.*

10. She was in 1915's *Peggy* and 1960's *Pepe.* She was also prominent in *A Bill of Divorcement, Dinner at Eight, Craig's Wife, The Great Ziegfeld, Topper, Parnell, The Wizard of Oz, Dulcy, The Man Who Came to Dinner* and *Father of the Bride.*

11. In 1929 he was in *Red Aces* and in 1954 he was in *World for Ransom.* He was also in *Springtime for Henry, Treasure Island, Jalna, She, The Charge of the Light Brigade, Kidnapped, Suez,* the Sherlock Holmes series, *Roxie Hart* and *Limelight.*

a) Mae Busch
b) Chester Conklin
c) Raymond Hatton
d) Nigel Bruce
e) Francis X. Bushman
f) Reginald Denny
g) Constance Collier
h) Billie Burke
i) Walter Catlett
j) Hobart Bosworth
k) Jane Darwell

18.   CHAMPION MS.

† † † † †

Match the woman with the sports accomplishment.

1.	Wilma Rudolph	a)	diving
2.	Babe Didrikson	b)	bowling
3.	Floretta McCutcheon	c)	ice-skating
4.	Glenna Collett Vare	d)	200 meters
5.	Ragnild Hveger	e)	80-meter hurdles
6.	Elizabeth Ryan	f)	tennis
7.	Elizabeth Robinson	g)	golf
8.	Dorothy Poynton Hill	h)	100 meters
9.	Fanny Blankers-Zeon	i)	swimming
10.	Vera Hruba Ralston		

† † †

19.   SURELY, YOU REMEMBER

† † † † †

1.   Who was known as "The King of Burlesque"?

* * *

2.   Who popularized the Black Bottom?

* * *

3.   Who was prosecuting attorney at the Scopes Monkey trial?

* * *

4. Who composed the music for *Psycho, North by North West, Vertigo* and *The Trouble With Harry?*

*   *   *

5. Who was the singing trumpet player who appeared in *Pennies from Heaven, Artists and Models, The Philadelphia Story, Cabin in the Sky, The Glenn Miller Story* and *The Five Pennies?*

*   *   *

6. Who was the son of the first Earl of Oxford who was an actor, director and scenarist?

*   *   *

7. Who was the heavyweight boxing champion and movie actor who was once married to Dorothy Dunbar?

*   *   *

8. Who won a special Oscar in 1927 for *The Patent Leather Kid?*

*   *   *

9. Whose band was known, at various times, as "America's Craziest Orchestra," "The Brown Derby Band," and "The Mad Musical Maniacs"?

*   *   *

10. Who was "King of the Banjo"?

† † †

20. COPS AND ROBBERS

1. Who played Lt. Monaghan in *Detective Story?*
2. Who played Ziggy in *Key Largo?*
3. Who played Ned Galloway in *The Criminal Code?*
4. Who was the warden in *The Criminal Code?*
5. Who produced *The Racket, Scarface* and *Macao?*
6. Who directed *The Big House?*
7. Whom did Lee Marvin scald with coffee in *The Big Heat?*
8. Who kills Ted Corsia with a spear gun in *Slightly Scarlet?*
9. Who played Silky in *Larceny?*
10. Who played Quinlan's assistant in *Touch of Evil?*

a) George Hill
b) Gloria Grahame
c) Dan Duryea
d) Joseph Calleia
e) Rhonda Fleming
f) Horace MacMahon
g) Marc Lawrence
h) Boris Karloff
i) Walter Huston
j) Howard Hughes

21. CRITICAL GUESSES, #1

† † † † †

What film is being reviewed?

1. "Karen Morley, Gilbert Roland and Lew Ayres lend steadying support to several less experienced but promising newcomers in the cast."—*Newsweek.*
2. "Frank Borzage has directed the film with a fine understanding of the delicate nuances, and Robert Taylor, Franchot Tone and Robert Young are splendid."—*New York Herald-Tribune.*
3. "In a closing speech to the çamera's eye Henry Fonda calls on the world to end the slaughter of civilians."—*Newsweek.*
4. "The two Englishmen abroad didn't want to be involved; they were eager to reach England in time for the cricket finals."—*New York Times.*
5. "Its principal characters are fictional in name only. Turrou, called Ed Renard, is played by Edward G. Robinson. Paul Lukas, Francis Lederer, George Sanders, Dorothy Tree and Lya Lys all portray actual people."—*Newsweek.*
6. "This melodrama is highlighted by some vividly realistic war scenes and James Cagney's characterization of a two-fisted toughie who cracks under the strain of fighting an enemy he can't get his hands on."—*Newsweek.*
7. "Marilyn Monroe and Anthony Caruso help lend a documentary effect to a lurid exposition."—*New York Herald-Tribune.*
8. "There are a few moments of extraordinary beauty in the film, such as little Ulysses asking Homer with infinite anxiety in a casual conversation not to leave home."—*New York Times.*
9. "You will find pleasant performances by Slim Summerville and Janet Gaynor, although Miss Gaynor is really too nice a person to be playing bad girls like Molly Larkin."—*New York Times.*

10. "That gorgeous example of bathing beauty art, Marilyn Monroe, cast as Miss Stanwyck's gay, excitement-craving future sister-in-law, is a real acting threat to the season's screen blondes."—*New York Post.*

a) *The Fighting 69th*
b) *The Asphalt Jungle*
c) *Blockade*
d) *Clash By Night*
e) *The Lady Vanishes*
f) *The Last Train from Madrid*
g) *The Human Comedy*
h) *Three Comrades*
i) *The Farmer Takes a Wife*
j) *Confessions of a Nazi Spy*

22. MEMORY PARADE

1. Who was "The Mystery Man of Europe" who was the sales agent for armament manufacturers during the 1920s?

* * *

2. What do Ralph Bellamy and Kirk Douglas have in common?

* * *

3. What was the favorite weapon of Kate Barker and George Kelly?

* * *

4. Doretta Morrow is the cousin of which singer?

29

5. Who was Blaze and why were wartime newspapers indignant over him?

* * *

6. Who was nominated for an Oscar as Best Supporting Actor for *Foreign Correspondent?*

* * *

7. What were the better-known names of John Blythe and Blanche Oelrichs?

* * *

8. Who was the Alabama actress once married to actor John Emery?

* * *

9. Who was Bill Baird's partner in their puppet act?

* * *

10. Scotty Beckett appeared in the Bowery Boys, Dead End Kids or Our Gang comedies?

† † †

23. BOSSES, #1

† † † † †

Match the boss and the bossed.

1. Dr. Zorba   a) Henry

2. Alan Brady   b) Tilda

3. Bruce Wayne   c) Mr. Roberts

4. Hercule Poirot   d) Dr. Ben Casey

5. The Baxters   e) Shorty

6. Charlie Chan   f) Rob Petrie

7. Boston Blackie   g) Hazel

8. Captain Morton   h) Alfred

9. Andy Gump   i) Birmingham Brown

10. Amos Burke   j) Capt. Arthur Hastings

† † †

Quiz-Word No. 2

ACROSS

1. He hit 60 in 1927 (4, 4).
5. Invented by Sir Arnold Lunn (6).
10. Deadly denizens of the deep (5, 4)
11. —— Ray Robinson (5).
12. His nickname was "Home Run," though the most he had in one season was only 12 (5).
13. Snodgrass was the —— of a World Series game (9).
14. Baseball star Moe Berg was also ——(10).
17. If Man O'War lost a race, he would have been an —— ran (4).
20. Dempsey was rough on a sparring ——(4).
21. The man in the net in ice hockey (4, 6).
22. Maurice McLoughlin was known in tennis as one (3, 6).
26. When Judge Landis became baseball czar, a lot of players went on this (5).
27. This lefty was a great pitcher (5).
28. *Down* —— *Way* (9).
30. What Connie Mack handed Owens before a game (6).
31. Grapples (8).

DOWN

1. John McGraw, for instance (8, 7).
2. Nickname of American League umpire Owens (5).
3. Babe Ruth's training methods weren't at all like this (8).
4. Notre Dame or the Yankees, for instance (5).
6. Rocky Marciano had none as heavyweight champ (6).
7. What the birler did (9).
8. Zapotek and Clarence DeMar (8, 7).
9. Song in 1913's *All Aboard* (4).
15. Jottings (9).
16. Producer's dream (1, 1, 1).
17. Red Grange hailed from the Univ. of —(3).
19. Detroit's hockey team (3, 5).
22. Pete Gray had an empty one on his baseball uniform (6).
24. *The* —— *The Yankees Lost the Pennant* (4).
25. Maris (5).
27. How to cause a third-degree burn (5).

32

24. CREDITS

† † † † †

Match the cast with the movie.

1. *Four Men and a Prayer*
2. *Hired Wife*
3. *No One Man*
4. *Gabriel Over the White House*
5. *Holiday*
6. *On the Riviera*
7. *The Green Goddess*
8. *Pan Americana*
9. *The Harvey Girls*
10. *The Pied Piper*
11. *Presenting Lily Mars*

a) Carole Lombard, Ricardo Cortez, Paul Lukas

b) Danny Kaye, Gene Tierney, Corinne Calvet

c) Philip Terry, Eve Arden, Robert Benchley, Audrey Long

d) Monty Woolley, Roddy McDowall, Otto Preminger, Anne Baxter, Peggy Ann Garner

e) Judy Garland, Van Heflin, Fay Bainter, Spring Byington

f) Loretta Young, Richard Greene, George Sanders, David Niven, C. Aubrey Smith

g) Walter Huston, Karen Morley, Franchot Tone

h) George Arliss, Alice Joyce, H. B. Warner, Ralph Forbes

i) Judy Garland, Ray Bolger, John Hodiak, Angela Lansbury, Preston Forster, Cyd Charisse

j) Rosalind Russell, Brian Aherne, Virginia Bruce, Robert Benchley, John Carroll

k) Katharine Hepburn, Cary Grant, Lew Ayres, Edward Everett Horton

† † †

25. LONG CAREERS

1. He was first seen in *Cleopatra* (1917) and last in 1957's *Affair in Reno*. He was also in *Pride of the Marines, The Amazing Dr. Clitterhouse, Million Dollar Legs, The Great McGinty, Adventures of Mark Twain, Brewster's Millions, Col. Effingham's Raid, The Secret Life of Walter Mitty*.

2. He debuted in 1911's *The Cowboy and the Lady* and left the screen after 1940's *Colt.45*. He was also in *Jane Eyre, Under Two Flags, The Four Horsemen of the Apocalypse, The Covered Wagon, Main Street, Rebecca of Sunnybrook Farm, Imitation of Life, It Happened One Night, Great Expectations, Stella Dallas* and *The Adventures of Robin Hood*.

3. He was in 1916's *The Real Thing at Last* and 1958's *Calabuch*. He also appeared in *The Skin Game, Good Companions, Sylvia Scarlett, Anthony Adverse, Parnell, A Yank at Oxford, Pride and Prejudice, Foreign Correspondent, Cheers for Miss Bishop, Charley's Aunt, Lassie Come Home, Keys to the Kingdom*, and *The Miracle on 34th Street*.

4. She was in *Lucky Day* (1929) and *Tiger by the Tail* (1969). She also appeared in *Little Caesar, I am a Fugitive from a Chain Gang, We're in the Money, Gold Diggers of 1935, Johnny Eager* and the "Torchy Blane" series.

5. He appeared in *Bubbles of Trouble* (1916) and in *Five Weeks in A Balloon* (1962). In between he was featured in "The Taxi Boys" series, *A Night at The Opera, The Outcasts of Poker Flat, The Toast of New York, Broadway Melody of 1938, The Firefly, Maytime, My Lucky Star, Angels With Dirty Faces, Destry Rides Again, the Great Dictator* and *Tin Pan Alley*.

6. He debuted in 1931's *Dreyfus* and was last seen in *The Magic Fountain*, 1964. He also appeared in *Becky Sharp, Things to Come, The Hunchback of Notre Dame, Tom Brown's School Days, The Moon is Down, The Cross of Lorraine, The Lodger, Wilson, The Keys of the Kingdom, I Remember Mama*.

7. She was seen in *The Cocoanuts*, 1929, and *What a Way to Go*, 1964. She was also in *Animal Crackers, Duck Soup, A Night at the Opera, A Day at the Races, The Big Store, Bathing Beauty, Up in Arms, The Horn Blows at Midnight* and *Auntie Mame*.

8. She first appeared in 1922's *Anna Ascends*, and was last seen in 1971's *Evel Knievel*. She was also in *Peter Pan, Ben Hur, The Singing Fool, The Midnight Patrol,* and *Pocketful of Miracles*.

9. In 1914 he was in *Lucille Love* and in 1953 in *The Marshal's Daughter*. He was also in *Stagecoach, Young Mr. Lincoln, Drums Along the Mohawk, The Ox-Bow Incident, Gilda, Hangover Square* and *My Darling, Clementine*.

10. He debuted in *Yes or No,* 1920, and was last in *The Last Hurrah,* 1958. His other movies include *A Free Soul, The Champ, The Thin Man, China Seas, Michael Strogoff, A Slight Case of Murder, The Great Profile,* and *The Bride Came C.O.D.*

a) Alan Hale Sr.
b) Betty Bronson
c) Edmund Gwenn
d) Francis Ford
e) Sir Cedric Hardwicke
f) Thurston Hall
g) Margaret Dumont
h) Glenda Farrell
i) Edward Brophy
j) Billy Gilbert

26. ALL STARS

1. Who was the pitcher who pitched only one game in the majors —a no-hitter?

2. Who was the ballplayer who was killed in a private plane when he drunkenly tried to take over the controls?

* * *

3. Who is the catcher holding the major league record for most games caught?

* * *

4. Who was the first major leaguer to enlist during World War II?

* * *

5. Who was the first former player to become a play-by-play radio announcer? The first major leaguer to go to bat wearing a number on his uniform? The first American League batter to confront pitcher Babe Ruth?

* * *

6. Who was the first major leaguer to be killed in World War I?

* * *

7. Who was the first National League player to make $100,000 a year?

* * *

8. Who won the American batting honors in odd years: 1921 (.394), 1923 (.403), 1925 (.393) and 1927 (.398)?

* * *

9. Who holds the National League record for most homers with bases loaded (14)?

* * *

10. Who sued organized baseball in the late 40s over the reserve clause?

27. SPONSORED BY

Match the advertising phrase and the advertiser.

1. "His master's choice"
2. "Ginger ale with piquant personality"
3. "They work while you sleep"
4. "Good for you and good to you"
5. "Has the edge 5 ways"
6. "Are you true to your type?"
7. "162 brushings in the 40-cent tube"
8. "Brewery goodness sealed right in"
9. "Delicious, nutritious, makes you feel ambitious"
10. "The main line airway"
11. "Years ahead in the science of flight"
12. "The great American family cereal"

a) Ry-Krisp
b) Listerine
c) Calo
d) Quaker Oats
e) Pabst
f) Cream of Wheat
g) Cliquot Club
h) United
i) Cascarets
j) Lockhead
k) Stetson
l) Pal

28. BADDIES

1. Who strangles himself in *The Brotherhood?*
2. Who was the nutty giggler in *House of Numbers?*
3. Who played a crooked lawyer in Nicholas Ray's *Party Girl?*

37

4. Who tempted Ann Dvorak in *Three On a Match?*
5. Who was obsessed with Belita in *The Gangster?*
6. Who was the spy chief in Garbo's *Mata Hari?*
7. Whom did Bill Bendix frame in *The Dark Corner?*
8. Who played the rackets boss in *Pete Kelly's Blues?*
9. Who ran the prison farm in *Unchained?*
10. Who played Chino in *The Wild One?*

a) Lyle Talbot
b) Edmond O'Brien
c) Mark Stevens
d) Lewis Stone
e) Lee Marvin
f) Chester Morris
g) Luther Adler
h) Barry Sullivan
i) Timothy Carey
j) Robert Taylor

† † †

29. CRITICAL GUESSES #2

† † † † †

What film is being reviewed?

1. "Never in his efforts before the camera has Mr. Chaney delivered such a marvelous performance as he does as this character." —*New York Times.*
2. "Linda Darnell is completely artificial and anomalous as the local siren." —*New York Times.*
3. "It certainly won't make Vichy happy—but that's just another point for it." —*New York Times.*
4. "Robert Walker is a newcomer who is so good as the sailor stranded with an Army unit that he is certain to go far on the screen." —*New York Herald-Tribune.*

5. "Picture is lifted from mediocrity through the intelligent acting and appeal of Sylvia Sidney. This legit girl makes her first screen appearance here as co-star with Gary Cooper." — *Variety.*

6. "Miss Hopkins makes Lily a very interesting person, who steals as another girl might sing." —*New York Times.*

7. "Miss Dietrich is a sultry siren, so inscrutable that even Laughton asks, 'What's the woman up to? What's her game?'" —*New York Herald-Tribune.*

8. "The Misses Crain and Blaine are beauts for whom Technicolor is a smart foil, and their voices are excellent for the Rodgers-Hammerstein type of composition."—*Variety.*

9. "Burgess Meredith plays the late fox-hole reporter with tremendous power and restraint." —*New York Herald-Tribune.*

10. "As the oppressed professor says, 'I've never prized safety, either for myself or my children. I've prized courage.'" — *New York Times.*

a) *The Story of G.I. Joe*
b) *Trouble in Paradise*
c) *Casablanca*
d) *State Fair*
e) *City Streets*
f) *The Thirteenth Letter*
g) *The Mortal Storm*
h) *Witness for the Prosecution*
i) *Bataan*
j) *He Who Gets Slapped*

30. MUSICMEN

† † † † †

Match the musician and the instrument.

1. Kid Ory   a) trombone
2. Johnny Dodds   b) guitar
3. Glenn Miller   c) trumpet
4. Oscar Moore   d) banjo
5. Mike Pingatore   e) drums
6. Stephen Grapelly   f) violin
7. Ray MacKinley   g) clarinet
8. Henry Busse
9. Phil Napoleon
10. Joe Venuti

† † †

31. SALES PITCHES

† † † † †

Match the slogan and the product.

1. "The famous skin softener"   a) Waterman
2. "It makes its mark around the world"   b) Ipana
3. "As gentle as human hands"   c) Fatima
4. "Save with safety, Shave with safety"   d) Campana
5. "Soap from trees—nature's gift to beauty"   Balm

6. "Head to foot, cellar to attic"

7. "Zip in every sip"

8. "Makes good foods taste better"

9. "Just enough Turkish"

10. "Workhorse of the skies"

11. "It's moisturized"

12. "Good for tender gums"

e) Douglas DC-3

f) Heinz catsup

g) Easy washing machines

h) Raleigh's

i) Spur

j) Palmolive

k) Gem

l) Fuller Brush

† † †

32. TV GHOSTS

† † † † †

1. Don Herbert taught what subject on TV?

* * *

2. What was the name of Jane Stacy's TV friend?

* * *

3. What was the name of the dance group on Jackie Gleason's show?

* * *

4. In pre-*Godfather* days, what was Pasquale's offer that Luigi ("Life With Luigi") always refused?

41

5. Pert Kelton played whose wife on "The Cavalcade of Stars"?

* * *

6. On "Kukla, Fran and Ollie," Beulah was a witch. What was Crackie?

* * *

7. Who was the hefty panelist on "It Pays to Be Ignorant"?

* * *

8. Who was that grumpy neurosurgical resident at County General?

* * *

9. Name at least two shows hosted by Jack Bailey.

* * *

10. At least two people must have gotten rich from "You'll Never Get Rich." Can you name the star and the creator of the show?

† † †

33. HOLLYWOOD PAIRS

† † † † †

Match the couples.

1. Nick Adams	a) Greg Bautzer
2. Dorothy Malone	b) Marty Melcher
3. Ronald Reagan	c) Lex Barker
4. Lana Turner	d) Jacques Bergerac
5. Marisa Pavan	e) Nancy Davis

42

6. Peggy Lee	f) Jean-Pierre Aumont
7. Doris Day	g) Phyllis Gates
8. Audie Murphy	h) Pam Archer
9. Dana Wynter	i) Dewey Martin
10. Rock Hudson	j) Carol Nugent

† † †

34. PHOTOPLAY NOTES

† † † † †

Match the cast with the movie.

1. *The Private Affairs of Bel Ami*

   a) Katharine Hepburn, Robert Young, Ralph Bellamy, Sidney Toler

2. *Spitfire*

3. *The Rage of Paris*

   b) Clifton Webb, Robert Wagner, Ruth Hussey, Debra Paget

4. *Stars and Stripes Forever*

   c) Jon Hall, Maria Montez, Turhan Bey, George Zucco

5. *Reckless*

   d) Jeff Chandler, Jack Palance, Martine Carol

6. *Sudan*

7. *The Return of Peter Grimm*

   e) Clark Gable, Myrna Loy, Spencer Tracy, Lionel Barrymore, Marjorie Maine

8. *Ten Seconds to Hell*

9. *Roughshod*

   f) George Sanders, Angela Lansbury, Ann Dvorak, Marie Wilson, Frances Dee

10. *Test Pilot*

   g) Danielle Darrieux, Douglas Fairbanks, Jr., Mischa Auer, Louis Hayward

h) Jean Harlow, William Powell, Franchot Tone, May Robson, Nat Pendleton

i) Lionel Barrymore, Helen Mack, Edward Ellis, Donald Meek

j) Robert Sterling, Claude Jarman, Jr., Gloria Grahame, Jeff Donnell

✝ ✝ ✝

35. SINGING MY WAY BACK HOME

✝ ✝ ✝ ✝ ✝

Match the singer and the song.

1. Ruth Etting   a) "Wheel of Fortune"

2. Kay Starr   b) "My Bill"

3. Eileen Barton   c) "Be My Love"

4. Clyde McCoy   d) "My Blue Heaven"

5. Hank Williams   e) "April Showers"

6. Julie London   f) "Shine On Harvest Moon"

7. Helen Morgan   g) "If I Knew You Were Coming I'd Have Baked A Cake"

8. Mario Lanza

9. Gene Austin   h) "Sugar Blues"

10. Al Jolson   i) "Hey, Good Looking"

                        j) "Cry Me a River"

✝ ✝ ✝

36. WHO?

1. Who won a special Academy Award in 1952?
2. Who replaced Bonar Law as British Prime Minister in 1923?
3. Who was married to Nan Sutherland, debuted in *Gentlemen of the Press* in 1929 and made his last movie (*The Furies*) in 1950?
4. Who was Ben Bernie's vaudeville partner?
5. Who was known as "The Arkansas Traveler"?
6. Who had been married to Ilka Chase, Julia Hout, Natalie Schaefer and Marianne Stewart?
7. Who played Inspector Lestrade in the Rathbone Sherlock Holmes movies?
8. Who served a prison term for manslaughter of his wife's first husband, Ray Raymond?
9. Who wrote "The World is Waiting for the Sunrise"?
10. Who created the role of Skipper in "The Toonerville Trolley" series?

a) Dennis Hoey
b) Paul Kelley
c) Gene Lockhart
d) Dan Mason
e) Harold Lloyd
f) Stanley Baldwin
g) Walter Huston
h) Phil Baker
i) Louis Calhern
j) Bob Burns

37. BOSSES, #2

† † † † †

Match the bosses and the bossed.

1. Sterling Morris
2. Daddy Warbucks
3. Mother
4. Admiral Sir Miles Messervy
5. Ben Cartwright
6. Chief Brandon
7. Mr. Bigdome
8. Martin Kane
9. Marcus Welby
10. Dr. Victor Frankenstein

a) Dick Tracy
b) Steven Kiley
c) Fritz
d) Happy McMann
e) Henry Tremblechin
f) Hop Sing
g) James Bond
h) Mrs. Emma Peel
i) Punjab
j) Billy Batson

† † †

38. HOLLYWOOD DIRECTORY

† † † † †

1. Who was married to Winifred Bryson and won an Oscar in 1929?

*   *   *

2. Who was the Lt. Governor of Nevada who was married to Clara Bow, and appeared in *The Man from Arizona* and *The Fighting Texans*?

3. Who was nominated for Best Supporting Actor Oscar in 1943, 1947, and 1948?

* * *

4. Who first appeared in 1902 in *The Messenger Boy's Mistake* and last in 1965 in *The Bounty Killer?*

* * *

5. Who first appeared in *Birth of a Nation,* 1914, and last in 1952, in *Carrie?*

* * *

6. Who was a Democratic Assemblyman in the California State Legislature and also was "Dr. Cyclops"?

* * *

7. Who was nominated for an Oscar as Best Actress in *Carmen Jones?*

* * *

8. Who played Denny in the Bulldog Drummond series?

* * *

9. Who was the nephew of a famous author and appeared in *Song of Russia, Spellbound, Arch of Triumph* and *Rhapsody?*

* * *

10. Who was married to Barry Thomson, Ralph Forbes and George Brent?

† † †

39. HALF-CAST

† † † † †

Complete the casting of these films.

1. *Tol'able David.* Forrest Robinson (Grandpa Hatburn), Ernest Torrence (Luke Hatburn), Walter P. Lewis (Iscah Hatburn) . . . who plays David Kineman?

* * *

2. *The Sun Also Rises.* Eddie Albert (Bill Gorton), Errol Flynn (Mike Campbell), Tyrone Power (Jake Barnes) . . . who plays Robert Cohn?

* * *

3. *The Front Page.* Walter Catlett (Murphy), Edward Everett Horton (Ben Singer), Pat O'Brien (Hildy Johnson) . . . who plays Walter Burns?

* * *

4. *Captain from Castile.* Thomas Gomez (Fr. Bartolome), Antonio Moreno (Don Francisco), John Sutton (Diego DeSilva), Lee J. Cobb (Juan Garcia), Tyrone Power (Pedro de Vargas) . . . who plays Cortez?

* * *

5. *Stanley and Livingstone.* Henry Hull (James Gordon Bennett, Jr.), Sir Cedric Hardwicke (Dr. Livingstone) . . . who plays Henry M. Stanley?

* * *

6. *Lightnin'.* J. M. Kerrigan (Lem Townstend), Jason Robards Sr. (Thomas) . . . who plays Lighnin' Bill Jones?

7. *In Old Chicago.* Brian Donlevy (Gil Warren), Andy Devine (Pickle Bixby), Don Ameche (Jack O'Leary) . . . who plays Dion O'Leary?

*   *   *

8. *Stella Dallas.* Lois Moran (Laurel Dallas), Beatrix Pryor (Mrs. Grosvenor), Alice Joyce (Helen Morrison) . . . who plays Stella Dallas?

† † †

40. BALL GAME MEMORIES

† † † † †

1. Who was the last manager of the St. Louis Browns?

*   *   *

2. Who replaced John McGraw as the New York Giants' manager?

*   *   *

3. Who managed the 1926 St. Louis Cardinals, when they won their first pennant?

*   *   *

4. Who was the manager of the 1914 Boston Braves—the "Miracle Braves"?

*   *   *

5. Who was the Brooklyn Dodgers' manager who noted that "nice guys finish last."?

*   *   *

6. Jimmie Dykes succeeded which manager?

*   *   *

7. Lynn Larry and $250,000 were traded to the Boston Red Sox by the Washington Senators for what manager-player?

*   *   *

8. Name the man who managed, off and on, the Washington Senators, the Detroit Tigers, the Boston Red Sox, the Philadelphia Phillies and the New York Yankees.

†   †   †

Quiz-Word No. 3

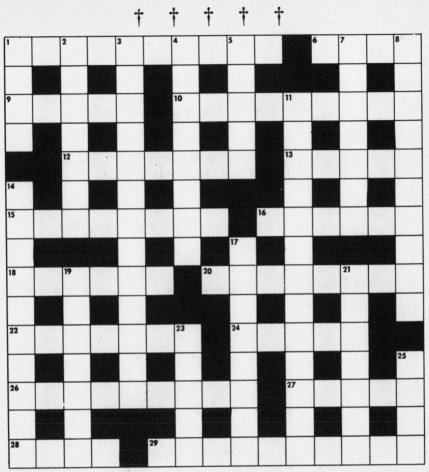

ACROSS
1. Mickey and Donald's creator (4, 6).
6. *Four Saints in Three* ——— (4)
9. Sinatra (5).
10. Gunga Din's formal clothes (4, 5).
12. "In the Cool Cool Cool of the ———" (7).
13. More pleasant (5).
15. Determined (8).
16. ——— *Highway* (6).
18. "——— -Hand Rose" (6).
20. Where I've been working on (8).
22. ——— *On the Wind* (7).
24. *The ——— That Failed* (5).
26. What Kildare often did (9).
27. *The ——— of New Orleans* (5).
28. "Willow—For Me" (4).
29. Dramatist (12).

DOWN
1. "Backstage ———" (4).
2. The Dorseys' occupations (7).
3. Wrote "Sophisticated Lady," etc. (4, 9).
4. Loners (8).
5. Supplementing (5).
7. Selections (7).
8. A musical direction (10).
11. Liberace could be called one (13).
14. Golf fanatic's wife? (5, 5).
17. Folksong poetry (8).
19. Weather conditions (7).
21. ——— *Of the Islands* (7).
23. Post ——— Drip (5).
25. *A ——— is Born* (4).

51

41. CINEMA BILL

† † † † †

Match the cast with the movie.

1. *Secrets of an Actress*

2. *Tight Little Island*

3. *See Here, Private Hargrove*

4. *Topaze*

5. *The Set-Up*

6. *Violent Saturday*

7. *The Shanghai Gesture*

8. *Wabash Avenue*

9. *Sin Town*

10. *Wagonmaster*

a) Robert Ryan, Audrey Totter, George Tobias, Alan Baxter

b) Gene Tierney, Walter Huston, Victor Mature, Maria Ouspenskaya

c) Constance Bennett, Broderick Crawford, Ward Bond, Andy Devine

d) Joanne Dru, Ward Bond, James Arness

e) Kay Francis, George Brent, Ian Hunter

f) Robert Walker, Donna Reed, Keenan Wynn, Robert Benchley

g) Basil Radford, Catharine Lacey, Joan Greenwood

h) John Barrymore, Myrna Loy, Reginald Mason

i) Victor Mature, Richard Egan, Lee Marvin

j) Betty Grable, Victor Mature, Phil Harris

† † †

42. LIFE'S WORK

Match the roles with the actress.

1. A poor Parisian girl, a tenement girl, an heiress, a princess, an Irish tomboy
2. Edgar Allen Poe's granddaughter, a manicurist, Belle Fawcett, Stella Kirby, a hat-checking aviatrix, a pseudo-Fanny Brice, Lillian Russell
3. Julie Rothschild, Robert Clive's wife, Richard the Lion Hearted's wife, the Empress Eugenie, a farmer's daughter, a bishop's wife
4. Sophie McDonald, Eve Harrington, Ben Hogan's wife, Nefretiti
5. Cri-Cri, Mary "Irish" O'Brien
6. Margy Frake, Gene Tierney's cousin, Dorothy Gish's daughter, William Holden's wife, Clifton Webb's oldest child
7. Kitty Vane, Ronald Colman's fiancee, a trapeze artist, Noah Beery's niece
8. Lionel Atwill's niece, Errol Flynn's fiancee, Queen Elizabeth's lady-in-waiting, General Custer's wife

a) June Haver
b) Alice Faye
c) Olivia de Havilland
d) Janet Gaynor
e) Jean Crain
f) Loretta Young
g) Anne Baxter
h) Vilma Banky

43. IN MEMORY OF

1. Who was the famed Mexican leader shot dead in 1923?

*   *   *

2. Who wrote "Keep the Home-Fires Burning"?

*   *   *

3. Who was the Russian surgeon famous for his rejuvenation experiments?

*   *   *

4. In 1941 J. Edgar Hoover decried what institution in these words: "a new home of disease, bribery, corruption, crookedness, rape, white slavery, thievery and murder."?

*   *   *

5. Between 1935 and 1940, the U.S. sold the Japanese how many tons of steel scrap: a) 10 million tons; b) 100 million tons; or c) 200 million tons?

*   *   *

6. Who wrote the tune to "It's All in the Game"?

*   *   *

7. The Hoover Moratorium of 1931 a) called a one-year halt on payment of all war debts due the U.S.; b) cancelled all government spending for a certain period; or c) changed the official names of undertakers to morticians.

*   *   *

8. What was the theme song of Earl Hines' orchestra?

* * *

9. Name two men for whom at least two cars apiece were named.

* * *

10. George Nelson was known as "Baby Face," Jack Diamond as "Legs." What was Alvin Karpis' nickname?

† † †

44. BOSSES, #3

† † † † †

Match the boss and underling.

1. The Bishop		a) Joe Mannix
2. Inspector Fenwick		b) Will Stutely
3. Julius Dithers		c) Michael Anthony
4. Commissioner Cary		d) Nikki Porter
5. Col. J. T. Hall		e) Lt. Uhura
6. Steve Wilson		f) Sgt. Ernie Bilko
7. James T. Kirk		g) Lorelei Kilbourne
8. Ellery Queen		h) The Gargoyle
9. John Beresford Tipton		i) Dudley Do-Right
10. Robin Hood		j) Dagwood Bumstead
11. Lou Wickersham		k) Capt. Video

† † †

45. FLICKERING MEMORIES

† † † † †

Match the cast with the film.

1. *The Walls of Jericho*
2. *Without Honor*
3. *Yankee Buccaneer*
4. *Arise, My Love*
5. *Beau James*
6. *The Blue Gardenia*
7. *Castle on the Hudson*
8. *The Champ*
9. *The Snows of Kilimanjaro*
10. *The Spirit of St. Louis*

a) Anne Baxter, Richard Conte, Ann Sothern, Raymond Burr, Jeff Donnell

b) John Garfield, Pat O'Brien, Ann Sheridan, Burgess Meredith

c) Cornel Wilde, Linda Darnell, Anne Baxter, Kirk Douglas, Henry Hull

d) Bob Hope, Vera Miles, Paul Douglas, Alexis Smith, Darren McGavin

e) Claudette Colbert, Ray Milland, Walter Abel, Dennis O'Keefe

f) Wallace Beery, Jackie Cooper, Irene Rich, Ed Brophy

g) Jeff Chandler, Scott Brady, Suzanne Ball, David Janssen

h) Laraine Day, Dane Clark, Franchot Tone, Agnes Moorhead

i) Gregory Peck, Susan Hayward, Ava Gardner, Hildegarde Neff

j) James Stewart, Patricia Smith

† † †

46. CRITICAL GUESSES, #3

† † † † †

What film is being reviewed?

1. "John Garfield is highly amusing singing a tough guy's version of 'Blues in The Night'." —*New York Times.*
2. "It took audacity to frame an arrant shocker in the terrible events of this terrible present, but Mr. Hitchcock and Mr. Wanger have had the nerve to do it." —*New York Herald-Tribune.*
3. "John Barrymore, who is singularly well suited to the role of the dignified, blase, bumptious dandy, delivers a performance that is a delight to the eye." —*New York Times.*
4. "Miss Tierney plays at being a brilliant and sophisticated advertising executive with the wild-eyed innocence of a college junior." —*New York Times.*
5. "Carole Lombard has never been better than in this, her screen farewell." —*Newsweek.*
6. "She is exquisite in the clothes which Eugenie made famous in the period, but the love she professed for de Lesseps never seems to glow." —*New York Daily News.*
7. "Mr. Kelly, who has a dancer's talents, has been pressed a bit too far in his first film role." —*New York Times.*
8. "Her work as the hardened, ever-scrapping ginmill entertainer serves pretty much as the teeterboard from which this picture flips itself from the level of the ordinary western into a class item." —*Variety.*
9. "As usual, Sturges has picked the actors where he found them, from familiar players to newcomers like Ella Raines." —*Newsweek.*
10. "The action occurs in the Sudetenland of 1938 and the family, though of German descent, is Czech by citizenship." —*New York Times.*

a) *Foreign Correspondent*
b) *Thank Your Lucky Stars*
c) *Four Sons*
d) *Hail the Conquering Hero*
e) *To Be or Not to Be*
f) *Laura*
g) *Beau Brummel*
h) *Destry Rides Again*
i) *For Me and My Gal*
j) *Suez*

47. CANVAS MEMORIES

1. In 1919 who won the heavyweight title from Jess Willard?

*   *   *

2. Before retiring in 1956, Rocky Marciano fought only one opponent who went 15 rounds with him. Who was he?

*   *   *

3. Who was "The Ambling Alp?" and what title did he win from Jack Sharkey?

*   *   *

4. Who did Joe Louis knock out in the 13th round at the Polo Grounds, June 18, 1941?

*   *   *

5. Floyd Patterson and Ingemar Johannson set what mark?

*   *   *

6. Joe Maxim lost the light-heavyweight title in December 1952 to whom?

*   *   *

7. What was the Joe Louis-Abe Simon fight of March 21, 1941, noted for?

*   *   *

8. The June 1930 bout for the vacant heavyweight championship was won by Max Schmeling. Who lost, and how did he lose?

*   *   *

9. At Shelby, Montana, Tom Gibbons met the heavyweight champion and lost. Who beat him and when?

*   *   *

10. Identify Clem McCarthy and Tex Rickard.

*   *   *

11. Who was the "Galveston Giant"?

*   *   *

12. What title did Sandy Saddler and Willy Pep hold?

†   †   †

48. CINEMATIC CRIME

† † † † †

1. Who played the prison farm warden in *The Mayor of Hell?*
2. Who wrote *Little Caesar, High Sierra* and *Scarface?*
3. Who played "Rolls" Royce in von Sternberg's *Underworld?*
4. Who played Machine Gun Kelly in the Corman movie?
5. Who smoothtalks Joan Crawford in *The Damned Don't Cry?*
6. Who is the hitman who kills William Holden in *The Turning Point?*
7. Who played the pioneer Mafia investigator in *Pay or Die?*
8. Who was the murderer tortured by teenage crime fighters in *This Day and Age?*
9. Who played the chief dope smuggler in *Port of New York?*
10. Who played the white-suited gunsel in *The Dark Corner?*

a) Ernest Borgnine
b) Charles Bickford
c) Charles Bronson
d) W. R. Burnett
e) James Cagney
f) Clive Brooks
g) Yul Brynner
h) William Bendix
i) David Brian
j) Neville Brand

† † †

49. ROGER CORMAN

† † † † †

Match the Roger Corman film with the cast.

1. *Five Guns West*
2. *The Day The World Ended*
3. *Swamp Women*
4. *The Oklahoma Woman*
5. *It Conquered the World*
6. *The Fall of the House of Usher*
7. *The Intruders*
8. *The Raven*
9. *The Man With the X-Ray Eyes*
10. *The Masque of the Red Death*

a) Vincent Price, Jane Asher
b) John Lund, Dorothy Malone
c) William Shatner, Robert Emhardt
d) Richard Denning, Lori Nelson
e) Vincent Price, Peter Lorre, Jack Nicholson
f) Beverly Garland, Marie Wilson
g) Richard Denning, Peggie Castle
h) Vincent Price, Myrna Fahey
i) Peter Graves, Lee Van Cleef
j) Ray Milland

† † †

50. COMMONERS

1. What do Lonnie Burr, Karen Pendleton, Cheryl Holdridge, Cubby O'Brien and Doreen Tracey have in common?

*   *   *

2. What did California Carlson, Lucky Jenkins, Windy Halliday and Johnny Nelson have in common?

*   *   *

3. What did Carl Denham, John Driscoll, Capt. Englehorn and Ann Darrow have in common?

*   *   *

4. What did the "Arizona", "Oklahoma" and "Utah" have in common?

*   *   *

5. What did John Larkin, Bartlett Robinson, Santos Ortega, Donald Briggs, Raymond Burr and Monte Markham have in common?

*   *   *

6. What did Jean Harlow, Mary Dees and Paula Winslow have in common?

*   *   *

7. What did Pete Martin, Baby Face Martin and Chuck Martin have in common?

*   *   *

8. What do Wyatt and Steve Rogers have in common?

* * *

9. What do Julie Newmar and Eartha Kitt have in common?

* * *

10. What did Ben W. Jones, Bro. John Payne, Dr. C. B. Hamann, Dr. Joseph C. Cyr, Dr. Robert L. French and Martin Godart have in common?

† † †

51. VIDEO VOCATIONS

† † † † †

1. Before Kojak and Kolchak there was Mike Kovac. Who played "The Man With a Camera"?

* * *

2. "Rootie Kazootie's" little friends were named what?

* * *

3. Who played a gambler at the end of his rope on "The Alcoa-Goodyear Theatre," thus winning an Emmy for the writers?

* * *

4. George Gobel was knocked off the tube by what western show?

* * *

5. Ted Key's cartoons in the *Saturday Evening Post* inspired what TV show?

6. Jayne Meadows of "I've Got a Secret" is the wife of which panelist of "What's My Line"?

*   *   *

7. Who flew around space in "The Galaxy"?

*   *   *

8. Richard Crenna played what role on "Our Miss Brooks"?

*   *   *

9. What was the name of the one-toothed character on "Kukla, Fran and Ollie"?

*   *   *

10. Alice Lon was the Champagne Lady with whose band?

†   †   †

Quiz-Word No. 4

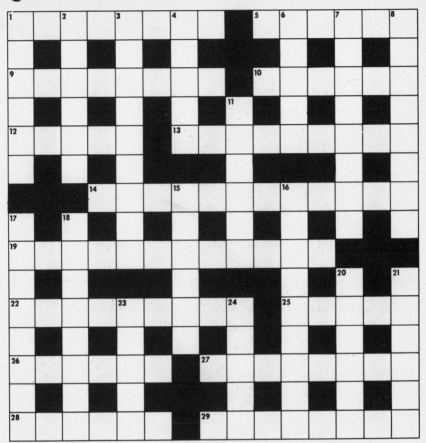

ACROSS

1. What anti-New Dealers called a WPA job (8).
5. ———— DeHaven (6).
9. Romberg song (8).
10. Moved along slowly (6).
12. What nostalgia does (5).
13. Arise (9).
14. Bert Parks emceed this show (4, 3, 5).
19. Atwater Kents picked this up (12).
22. Candid (9).
25. Heather ———— (5).
27. He appeared in *The Lemon Drop Kid, Dinner at Eight, The Best Man,* etc. (3, 5).
28. High regard (6).
29. Claghorn was ———— (1, 7).

DOWN

1. Joan to Constance (6).
2. Limited (6).
3. Participants did this on quiz shows (9).
4. AM-FM (5).
6. "Hawaii Calls" locale, among others (5).
7. What a show would do before it went on the air (8).
8. Participating group on many shows (8).
11. "How Much is That Doggie in the Window?" was one (3, 3).
15. Baby Snooks specialty (6).
16. "———— Merry-Go-Round" (9).
17. Status, alas, of many memorable things (8).
18. Ballplayers and movie stars sign it—and break it (8).
20. How "Inner Sanctum" was supposed to have left us (6).
21. Orson Welles' Mercury cast-member (6).
23. Radio research survey (5).
24. Coward's Christmas carols? (5).

52. DOUGLAS FAIRBANKS, JR.

1. Whom did he marry when he was 19? What movie did they make together at this point?

* * *

2. Who played the flight commander in *The Dawn Patrol?*

* * *

3. Who played Catherine the Great to his Peter III?

* * *

4. What movie did he make with Gertrude Lawrence?

* * *

5. What role did he have in *The Prisoner of Zenda?*

* * *

6. Who played his brother in *The Corsican Brothers?*

* * *

7. What role did he play in *The Exile?*

* * *

8. Who played the countess in *That Lady in Ermine?*

53. MOTION PICTURE RELICS

† † † † †

Match the cast with the movie.

1. *Baby Face Nelson*
2. *Young Mr. Pitt*
3. *Will Success Spoil Rock Hunter?*
4. *Waterloo Bridge*
5. *What a Life*
6. *The Conspirators*
7. *Charlie Chan in Rio*
8. *The Breaking Point*
9. *Billy the Kid*
10. *Colleen*

a) Jayne Mansfield, Tony Randall, Joan Blondell, John Williams

b) Mickey Rooney, Carolyn Jones, Sir Cedric Hardwicke, Jack Elam

c) Robert Donat, Robert Morley, Phyllis Calvert, John Mills

d) Vivien Leigh, Robert Taylor, C. Aubrey Smith

e) John Garfield, Patricia Neal, Phyllis Thaxter, Wallace Ford

f) Sidney Toler, Mary Beth Hughes, Cobina Wright, Jr., Victor Jory

g) Johnny Mack Brown, Wallace Beery, Kay Johnson, Karl Dane

h) Hedy Lamarr, Paul Henreid, Sydney Greenstreet, Peter Lorre

i) Dick Powell, Ruby Keeler, Joan Blondell, Hugh Herbert, Jack Oakie

j) Jackie Cooper, Betty Field, Lionel Stander, Hedda Hopper

† † †

54. SEVENTH INNING STRETCH

† † † † †

1. Chicago White Soxer Ted Lyons pitched for how many years?

* * *

2. Name the odd man out: Larry French, Rube Waddell, Eddie Plank, Grover Cleveland Alexander, Herb Pennock.

* * *

3. For what team was Lefty Grove pitching when he won 152 games, lost 41 for the years 1928 through 1933?

* * *

4. Who set a batting average of .424 in 143 games in 1924?

* * *

5. Who was the Washington Senator who won the AL batting championship in 1928 with .379?

* * *

6. Which team won 110 of the 154 games it played in a season? Which season was it?

* * *

7. Who was the Brooklyn Dodgers pitcher who hit into a triple play and a double play successively in the fifth game of the 1920 World's Series?

* * *

8. Who made a triple play unassisted in the 1920 World's Series?

* * *

9. Elroy Face did what for the Pittsburgh Pirates in 1959?

*   *   *

10. In 1920 and 1922, what did George Sisler accomplish for the St. Louis Browns?

†   †   †

55. HOLLYWOOD TRAGEDIES #2

†   †   †   †   †

1. Who was the actress who jumped from a window to her death in 1939? She was Monte Banks' ex-wife and had appeared in *Let No Man Put Asunder* and *Inspiration.*

*   *   *

2. Who was the actor who shot himself in 1939? He had debuted in 1921 in *Little Lord Fauntleroy,* and his credits included *Alice Adams, Seven Sinners, Little Shepherd of Kingdom Come, Tess of the Storm Country, A Tale of Two Cities* and *A Yank at Oxford.*

*   *   *

3. Who was the 36-year-old dancer-choreographer who died of pneumonia and diabetes in 1964? She had appeared in *Kiss Me Kate* and *Pajama Game.*

*   *   *

4. Who was the 22-year-old actress who died of cancer, after injuring her right knee while filming *East of Sumatra,* and refusing amputation when the injury became malignant.

*   *   *

5. Who was the Hungarian actress who hanged herself in 1941? She and her twin sister had a famous dancing act.

*   *   *

6. Who were the twin brothers (*Our Gang*) who, at the age of 19, died in a 1934 flood?

*   *   *

7. Who was the 24-year-old actress who jumped off the "Hollywoodland" sign the same year she appeared in *Thirteen Women?*

*   *   *

8. Who was the 25-year-old actor who was injured in an explosion while filming *What Price Glory* and died two years later from the effects?

*   *   *

9. Who was the 40-year-old actor ("Rawhide") who drowned in Peru?

*   *   *

10. Who was the actress who was murdered by her son in 1939? She was once married to Josef Swickard, and had appeared in such movies as *Children of Divorce* and *Legally Dead.*

*   *   *

11. Who was the 26-year-old singer-actor who was accidentally shot in 1934?

*   *   *

12. Who was the 27-year-old actor (*The Lodger*) who died of a heart attack in 1944, as the result of a crash diet?

*   *   *

13. Who was the Scandinavian actor (*The Big Parade, The Son of the Sheik*) who shot himself in 1934?

*   *   *

14. Who was the 43-year-old actress *(The Egyptian)* who gassed herself in September, 1971?

†   †   †

56. SILVER SCREEN VETERANS

†   †   †   †   †

Match the credits and the name.

1. He first appeared in 1915's *Don Quixote* and last in 1955's *Run for Cover*. He also appeared in *Tess of the Storm Country, So Big, Stella Dallas, The Greater Glory, Abie's Irish Rose, Sin of Madelon Claudet, Grand Hotel, Dinner at Eight, Meet Dr. Christian* and *Dancing in the Dark.*

2. In 1921 he was in *The Man Turner* and in 1964 in *Man's Favorite Sport.* He was also in *The Jazz Singer, Dirigible, Ladies of the Big House, I am A Fugitive From a Chain Gang, One Way Passage, 20,000 Years in Sing Sing, It Happened One Night, Alibi Ike, Cain and Mabel, Woman of the Year,* and *Texas, Brooklyn, and Heaven.*

3. He was in *Tarzan of the Apes* (1918) as well as *How to Succeed in Business Without Really Trying* (1967). He also appeared in *The Ten Commandments, The Big Parade, King of Kings, The Four Feathers, Sign of the Cross, King Kong, The Emperor Jones, Green Pastures, The Thief of Bagdad, Cabin in the Sky, Anna Lucasta* and *Elmer Gentry.*

4. He was in 1922's *A Front Page Story* and 1970's *Cold Turkey.* He also was in *Ruggles of Red Gap, The Front Page, The Gay Divorcee, Top Hat, Lost Horizon, Shall We Dance, Here Comes Mr. Jordan, I Married An Angel,* and *Arsenic and Old Lace.*

5. He was in 1914's *A Cigarette—That's All* and in 1951's *Across The Wide Missouri.* He also was seen in *Submarine, Dirigible, The Littlest Rebel, Laddie, They Were Expendable, The Treasure of the Sierra Madre* and *Task Force.*

6. This actor was in 1912's *Hoffmeyer's Legacy* and in 1949's *My Dream is Yours.* He was also in *Tillie's Punctured Romance, The Leather Pushers, Two Tars,* the "Mr. Average Man" series, *Kid Millions, Twentieth Century, San Francisco, Three Men On a Horse, Hollywood Hotel* and *Mad Wednesday.*

7. In 1926 he debuted in *The Quarterback* and in 1968 he closed out his career in *Buckskin.* He also appeared in *The Cocoanuts, The G-Men, Case of the Curious Bride, Page Miss Glory, Bullets or Ballots, San Quentin, Melody Ranch, Dr. Jekyll and Mr. Hyde, The Maltese Falcon, High Sierra, The Treasure of The Sierra Madre* and *The Glenn Miller Story.*

8. In 1913 he was in *The Redemption of David Carson* and in 1952 he was in *Lone Star.* He was also in *The Spoilers, The Sign of the Cross, Les Miserables, Ben Hur, If I Were King, A Connecticut Yankee, The Crusades, Santa Fe, Cheers for Miss Bishop* and *Samson and Delilah.*

9. In 1920 he was in *The Call of the Road* and in 1959 in *The Sea Fury.* In between he appeared in *The Unholy Three, King of the Khyber Rifles, The Black Watch, The Lost Patrol, The Informer, Under Two Flags, Wee Willie Winkle, Gunga Din, Call Out the Marines* and *The Quiet Man.*

10. He was in *An Unseen Enemy* (1912) and in *Red River* (1948). He was also in *Judith of Bethulia, The Prisoner of Shark Island, Kid Galahad, Souls at Sea, Mr. Smith Goes to Washington, They Knew What They Wanted* and *Duel in The Sun.*

a) Roscoe Karns
b) Jean Hersholt
c) Rex Ingram
d) Jack Holt
e) Harry Carey
f) Edward Everett Horton
g) Barton MacLane

h) Victor McLaglen
i) Edgar Kennedy
j) William Farnum

57.   AFTERTHOUGHTS

1.   What tragedy was reported in these words: "It's bursting into flames! Get that shot! Get that shot! It's crashing, crashing, terrible, oh, my, get out of the way, please. It's burning, bursting into flames and is falling on the mooring paths and all the people agree this is one of the terrible, worst tragedies in the world! Oh, the humanity. . . ."

* * *

2.   Where was Alvin Karpis captured?

* * *

3.   Who wrote *Try and Stop Me?*

* * *

4.   Who wrote *The Snake Pit?*

* * *

5.   Who wrote *King's Row?*

* * *

6.   Who was our Ambassador to Japan just before Pearl Harbor?

* * *

7. Mt. Suribachi is on what Pacific island?

* * *

8. Who were Messrs. Kuruso and Nomura?

* * *

9. "The Prince of Wales" was the scene of an important treaty signing in 1941. What was the treaty and who were the signators?

* * *

10. What was Ike's rank when he was appointed commander of U.S. forces in Europe?

† † †

58. BOOB TUBE TIME

† † † † †

1. Who played Lily Ruskin?

* * *

2. Who played Blanche Morton?

* * *

3. Who played Dobie Gillis?

* * *

4. Who played Lily Munster?

* * *

5. Who played Gidget?

* * *

6.   Who invented a knife on "The Adventures of Jim Bowie"?

*   *   *

7.   Who was Cain on "Cain's Hundred"?

*   *   *

8.   Who starred in the TV version of "The Asphalt Jungle"?

*   *   *

9.   Who played a lady cop on "Decoy"?

*   *   *

10.   Who was the man on "The Tightrope"?

† † †

59.   MIND-JOGGING

† † † † †

1.   What did Sylvia Hawkes, Kay Spreckels, Rhea Langham, Carole Lombard and Josephine Dillon have in common?

*   *   *

2.   Who played the dying French soldier in *All Quiet on the Western Front?*

*   *   *

3.   Deanna Durbin, Barbara Read and Nan Grey played sisters in what movie?

*   *   *

4. Frank Morgan played whose guardian in *Dimples?*

* * *

5. Name the 1940 prison picture starring Pat O'Brien, Ann Sheridan and John Garfield.

* * *

6. Will Rogers, Evelyn Venable, Kent Taylor, Louis Dresser and Stepin Fetchit starred in what 1934 picture?

* * *

7. Name William S. Hart's horse.

* * *

8. Richard Dix, William Collier, Jr., and Irene Dunne appeared together in what 1931 movie?

* * *

9. In *Boys Town*, Pee Wee is hit by a car. Who played Pee Wee?

* * *

10. Who is the villain in *Shadow of a Doubt?*

† † †

60. HOLLYWOOD PAIRS #2

† † † † †

Match the couples.

1. Arlene Dahl
2. Ida Lupino
3. Russ Tamblyn
4. Jane Powell
5. Laurence Olivier
6. Jose Ferrer
7. Pier Angeli
8. ZaZa Gabor

a) Pat Nerney
b) Venetia Stevenson
c) Fernando Lamas
d) Vic Damone
e) George Sanders
f) Howard Duff
g) Rosemary Clooney
h) Vivien Leigh

† † †

61. DUGOUT CHATTER

† † † † †

1. Who won his 300th game in 1963 as a major league pitcher—the only game he won that year?

* * *

2. In 1944 The Blue Jays was selected as the alternate name for which team?

* * *

3. Grover Cleveland pitched 90 shutouts. Who pitched more? How many?

* * *

4. In what year did Joe DiMaggio hit 46 homers?

* * *

5. Pepper Martin played for what team when he stole five bases and batted .500 in a World Series? What World Series?

* * *

6. Who was the Detroit Tigers' pitcher who won 194 season games and four World Series games?

* * *

7. Harry Breechen won three of the four games won by St. Louis Cards in what World Series?

* * *

8. Jimmie Fox and Joe Hauser hold what records for the Philadelphia A's?

* * *

9. Who was the outfielder who made more than 4,000 hits in his career?

* * *

10. Allie Reynolds pitched two no-hitters in 1951. Who did the same in 1952?

† † †

62. CRITICAL GUESSES, #4

† † † † †

What film is being reviewed?

1. "A newcomer, Sonny Tufts, practically steals acting honors with his portrayal of a happy-go-lucky soldier from Kansas." —*New York Herald-Tribune.*

2. "Chico was shy as a young man might be shy, and Diane's shyness was a trembling sweet thing to see." —*National Board of Review.*

3. "Dana Andrews has the chief role of Sergeant Tyne." —*New York Herald-Tribune.*

4. "Paulette Goddard, a winsome waif attired almost throughout in short ragged dress and bare legs above the knees, is naturally introduced. She registers handily." —*Variety.*

5. "Miss Swanson gives a lively portrayal." —*New York Times.*

6. "The romance is handled superlatively by Teresa Wright and Richard Ney." —*New York Herald-Tribune.*

7. "Watch Bob Hope, the most persistently perplexed man on the screen, tearing himself to pieces." —*New York Times.*

8. "For goodness sakes, what makes Captain Thorndike run?" —*New York Times.*

9. "It is altogether fitting that the greatest admiral ever to lead an English fleet at this moment should be pictured with profound affection and respect on the screen." —*New York Times.*

10. "Alla Nazimova is splendid as the actress." —*New York Herald-Tribune.*

a) *That Hamilton Woman*
b) *Mrs. Miniver*
c) *A Walk in The Sun*
d) *Escape*
e) *Caught in The Draft*
f) *Modern Times*
g) *So Proudly We Hail*
h) *Man Hunt*
i) *Madame Sans-Gene*
j) *Seventh Heaven*

† † †

79

† † † † †

ACROSS

1. "Queen for ———" (1,3).
3. Shaw or O'Neill (10)
10. Babe Ruth now occupies one in Coopperstown's Hall of Fame (5).
11. Culbertson played on this (9).
12. Holman or Beckman (8, 6)
14. Revered (7).
15. Contested (7).
18. Maureen O'Hara or Rhonda Fleming (7).
20. Crystal ball viewer (7).
21. A Depression job (3, 5, 6).
25. Henry Aldrich (4, 5).
26. "Hoobert Heever," for example (5).
27. His theme song: "Ciribiribin" (5, 5).
28. A movie is filmed on ——— (1,3).

DOWN

1. Originally Harriette Lake (3, 7).
2. What happened to many Dust Bowl farms (9).
4. "Open the Door, ———" (7).
5. Marlene Dietrich film (7).
6. Complete (6).
7. Jewish clergyman (5).
8. *East of* ——— (4).
9. Family tree (8).
13. British Tommy, North African campaign (1, 6, 3).
16. *The Jolson Story* ——— *Jolson Sings Again* (8).
17. What does a femme do with a fan? (3, 6).
19. Red Grange got his from the University of Illinois (7).
20. ———, *Private Hargrove* (3, 4).
22. Employer (5).
23. Test (5).
24. "——— Parker," radio show set in Jonesport, Me. (4).

† † †

Quiz-Word No. 5

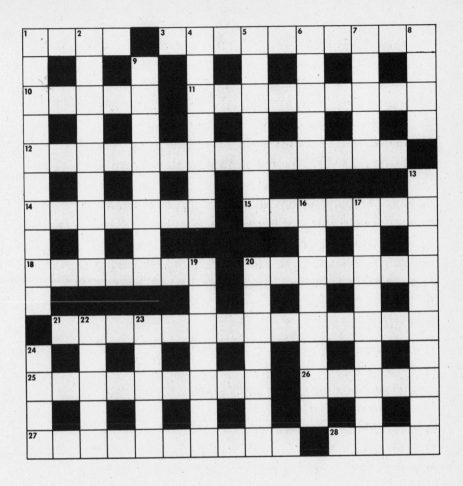

63. CAST THE MOVIE #1

† † † † †

1. Ginger Rogers, David Niven, Charles Coburn and Ernest Truex
2. Anna May Wong, Dan Seymour and Richard Loo
3. Bud Abbott, Lou Costello and Nat Pendleton
4. Charles Boyer, Lauren Bacall, Peter Lorre , and Katina Paxinou
5. Loretta Young, Barry Sullivan and Bruce Cowling
6. Fred Astaire, George Burns, Gracie Allen and Joan Fontaine
7. Jean Arthur, Marlene Dietrich and John Lund
8. William Bendix, Susan Hayward, John Loder and Alan Napier
9. John Mills, Sally Ann Howes and Diane Churchill
10. Kenny Delmar, Una Merkel, June Lockhart and Kenneth Farrell

a) *It's a Joke, Son*
b) *The Hairy Ape*
c) *Bachelor Mother*
d) *A Damsel in Distress*
e) *Buck Privates*
f) *Confidential Agent*
g) *The History of Mr. Polly*
h) *A Foreign Affair*
i) *Bombs Over Burma*
j) *Cause for Alarm*

† † †

64. RETENTION SKILLS

† † † † †

1. What building replaced New York's Old Waldorf-Astoria Hotel?

* * *

2. Who disappeared with navigator Fred Noonan in 1937?

* * *

3. Who wrote the column "Pitching Horseshoes"?

* * *

4. "Time and the Fate of Man" was the name of what item at the 1939 World's Fair?

* * *

5. What was the name of the model city at the 1939 World's Fair?

* * *

6. What two Boston nightclubs were the scenes of great disasters?

* * *

7. Who said, "Hitler has missed the bus"?

* * *

8. Who wrote these lines: "We'll use a signal I have tried and found far-reaching and easy to yell. Waa-hoo!"?

* * *

9. Who said, "Let's look at the record"?

*   *   *

10. Who was the French singer associated with "La Vie en Rose"?

†   †   †

65. CHANNEL CROSSINGS

†   †   †   †   †

1. All in all, Teddy Nadler won: a) $50,000; b) $100,000; or c) over $250,000 on quiz shows?

*   *   *

2. What town is the locale of "Search for Tomorrow"?

*   *   *

3. Who led the band on "Super Circus"?

*   *   *

4. Who wrote the theme music for Hal March's "The Bachelors"?

*   *   *

5. What did Russ Hodges, Jack Drees and Don Dunphy have in common?

*   *   *

6. Who played "Rod Brown of the Rocket Rangers"?

*   *   *

7. Who starred on "Saturday Night Revue"?

* * *

8. Who were the Canadian comics often featured on Ed Sullivan's show?

* * *

9. What did Don Carter, Ned Day and Buzz Fazio have in common?

* * *

10. Who played the character of Harvey Weskit?

† † †

66. WRITERS CRAMP

† † † † †

Who wrote

1. *When We Were Very Young*

* * *

2. *Those Barren Leaves*

* * *

3. *Arrowsmith*

* * *

4. *The Great Gatsby*

* * *

85

5.   *Barren Ground*

*   *   *

6.   *Here Comes the Bride*

*   *   *

7.   *A Son of His Father*

*   *   *

8.   *The Red Lamp*

*   *   *

9.   *The Crystal Cup*

*   *   *

10.   *Dark Laughter*

†   †   †

67. MOVIESVILLE

† † † † †

Match the movie, the director and the description.

1. *The House of the Seven Gables*   a) George Sidney
2. *Madam Satan*   b) Preston Sturges
3. *Pat and Mike*   c) Mark Robson
4. *Queen Christina*   d) Arch Oboler
5. *The Saxon Charm*   e) Rouben Mamoulian
6. *The Seventh Victim*   f) Joe May
7. *The Story on Page One*   g) Claude Minyon
8. *Key to the City*   h) C. B. De Mille
9. *Bwana Devil*   i) George Cukor
10. *The Great Moment*   j) Clifford Odets

    I. Robert Montgomery as a producer; John Payne as a play-wright; Susan Hayward as his wife.

    II. Lillian Roth, Reginald Denny, and Roland Young at a Zeppelin party.

    III. Ancestor of *Rosemary's Baby*. With Kim Hunter, Tom Conway, Hugh Beaumont.

    IV. Joel McCrea and Betty Field and the invention of an anaesthetic.

    V. His Honor Clark Gable and Her Honor Loretta Young meet in Frisco.

    VI. Tony Franciosa defends Rita Hayworth and Gig Young.

    VII. George Sanders and Vincent Price in a Hawthorne tale.

    VIII. Tracy and Hepburn as trainer and athlete.

    IX. Garbo and Gilbert as Swedish queen and lover.

    X. Robert Stack and Barbara Britton fight lions in 3-D.

† † †

68. DOCTOR'S EXAM

† † † † †

Match the doctor and the actor.

1. Dr. Huer	a) Richard Boone
2. Dr. IQ	b) Peter Sellers
3. Dr. Sean Jamison	c) Brian Keith
4. Dr. James Kildare	d) Edgar Stehli
5. Dr. Konrad Styner	e) Ed Nelson
6. Dr. No	f) David Janssen
7. Dr. Kimble	g) Lew Valentine
8. Dr. Rossi	h) Joel McCrea
9. Dr. Strangelove	i) Joseph Wiseman
10. Dr. Christian	j) Jean Hersholt

† † †

69. BIG-LEAGUE ALIAS

† † † † †

Match the baseball nickname with the real name.

1. Irish	a) Branch Rickey
2. Don	b) Hubert Pruett
3. Nap	c) Charles H. Root
4. Schoolboy	d) George N. Rucker
5. Buddy	e) Cletus Poffenberger
6. Chinski	f) Lynwood Rowe
7. Jeptha	g) Warren U. Rosar

8. Mahatma	h) Charles F. Rhem
9. Flint (or Shad)	i) Emil Meusel
10. Chief	j) Harold Reiser
11. Pistol Pete	k) Frederick Rudolph
12. Shucks	l) Eppa R. Rixey
13. Boots	m) Allie P. Reynolds
14. Babe	n) Earnest Phelps

70. PEN-AND-INK SOLDIERS

What branch of the service did these characters join during World War II?

1. Harold Teen

2. Joe Palooka

3. Slats

4. Snuffy Smith

5. Barney Google

6. Dick Tracy

7. Mickey Finn

8. Scorchy Smith

9. Tillie the Toiler

71. GEORGE SANDERS

† † † † †

Match the George Sanders role with the movie.

1. *Lloyds of London*
2. *Rebecca*
3. *The Picture of Dorian Gray*
4. *The Fan*
5. *All About Eve*
6. *Ivanhoe*
7. *Moonfleet*

a) Jack Favell
b) Lord Darlington
c) Addison de Witt
d) Lord Ashwood
e) Lord Everett Stacy
f) Lord Henry Wooton
g) Sir Brian de Bois-Gilbert

† † †

72. CAST THE MOVIE #2

† † † † †

1. Dane Clark, Janis Paige, Zachary Scott and Faye Emerson
2. Clark Gable, Lana Turner, Anne Baxter, John Hodiak and Ray Collins
3. John Wayne, William Holden and Constance Towers
4. Orson Welles, Joseph Cotten, Dolores Del Rio and Agnes Moorehead
5. Shirley Temple, Jerome Courtland, Walter Abel and Robert Benchley
6. Jean Arthur, John Wayne, Charles Winninger and Phil Silvers
7. Jack Benny, Fred Allen and Mary Martin
8. Ann Sothern, Robert Young, Ruth Hussey and George Tobias

9. George Raft, Lynn Bari and Virginia Huston
10. Richard Widmark, Jean Peters and Thelma Ritter

a) *Kiss and Tell*
b) *The Horse Soldiers*
c) *Her Kind of Man*
d) *Pickup on South Street*
e) *A Lady Takes a Chance*
f) *Maisie*
g) *Homecoming*
h) *Journey into Fear*
i) *Nocturne*
j) *Love Thy Neighbor*

† † †

73. TIMELY IDENTIFICATION

† † † † †

In *Literary Digest,* November 24, 1934, the following people are discussed. Match their names with the reason for their prominence at the time.

1. Joseph W. Byrnes   a) Chancellor of Austria

2. Josephine Roche   b) Composer-conductor

3. Richard Whitney   c) U.S. Ambassador to Mexico

4. Francis W. Biddle   d) President of N.Y. Stock Exchange

5. Tom Mooney   e) Alaska explorer

6. Harold Clayton Urey   f) President of National League

g) Author

7. Josephus Daniels   h) Democratic floor leader, House of Representatives

8. Kurt Schuschnigg

9. Peggy Bacon   i) Assistant Secretary of Treasury

10. Ford C. Frick   j) Chairman, NLRB

11. Rev. Bernard R.   k) Convicted bomber
    Hubbard
                     l) Discoverer of heavy water

12. Albert Coates

† † †

74. RADIO ECHOES

1. Who originally sang Jack Benny's theme song, "Love in Bloom," in the movies?

* * *

2. Who was lead singer of The Ink Spots?

* * *

3. What was Fletcher Henderson's theme song?

* * *

4. Name four radio shows starring Frank Sinatra.

* * *

5. Who were the Quarrymen?

* * *

6. Scrappy Lambert, Bob Moody, Tubby Weyant and Leonard Stokes were featured on what show?

* * *

7. Who used "Good-night, Sweetheart" as a sign-off song?

* * *

8. Who was the announcer on the 1932 radio show "Music That Satisfies"?

* * *

9. What musical instruments did Muriel and Vee play?

* * *

10. Who was the "Poet of the Organ"?

† † †

✝ ✝ ✝ ✝ ✝

ACROSS

1. *New York Herald-Tribune* columnist (6, 7).
2. What Harlow Wilcox and Harry Von Zell would do (9).
11. *The Good* ——— (5).
12. Popular pub game (5).
13. Lindbergh was a ——— in 1927 (9).
14. Silent screen performers tried to make theirs highly visible (8).
16. Shirley Temple was ——— by her fans (6).
19. Dillinger (6).
20. A Spanish dance (8).
22. Mata Hari ——— her victims (9).
24. To desire eagerly (5).
25. How many times were you beaten to the bar? (5).
26. The first to break the four-minute mile (9).
27. People who take care of card table (6, 7).

DOWN

2. Listening time for soaps (9).
3. ——— Shor, restaurateur and Broadway character (5).
4. Hardship (8).
5. Frigidair competitor (6).
6. Shut out (9).
7. Jackie Gleason's bartender character wore one (5).
8. The Rockin' Chair Lady (7, 6).
9. Broadcasting's heavenly bodies (3, 5, 5).
15. Introduced (9).
17. Winchellism for a Nevada divorcee (9).
18. Sally Rand's specialty (3, 5).
21. Gum (6).
23. Tammany ——— (5).
24. "Our Gang" gangster (5).

✝ ✝ ✝

Quiz-Word No. 6

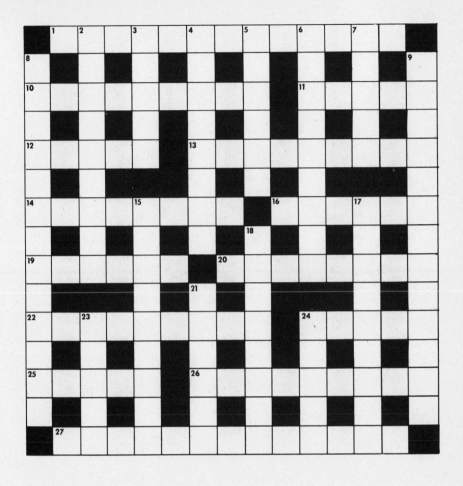

75. THE MOVING PICTURE GLIDE

† † † † †

Match the cast with the film.

1. *Smilin' Through*

2. *Sorrowful Jones*

3. *Sylvia Scarlett*

4. *Three Strangers*

5. *Treasure Island*

6. *Under Capricorn*

7. *Walk Softly, Stranger*

8. *The Web*

9. *Wild is the Wind*

10. *The Big Land*

a) Alan Ladd, Virginia Mayo, Edmund O'Brien, Julie Bishop

b) Ingrid Bergman, Joseph Cotten, Michael Wilding, Margaret Leighton

c) Anna Magnani, Anthony Quinn, Anthony Franciosa, Dolores Hart

d) Jeanette MacDonald, Brian Aherne, Gene Raymond, Ian Hunter

e) Ella Raines, Edmond O'Brien, William Bendix, Vincent Price

f) Bob Hope, Lucille Ball, William Demarest

g) Katharine Hepburn, Cary Grant, Brian Aherne, Edmund Gwenn

h) Sydney Greenstreet, Geraldine Fitzgerald, Peter Lorre

i) Wallace Beery, Jackie Cooper, Lewis Stone, Lionel Barrymore, Otto Kruger

j) Joseph Cotten, Valli, Spring Byington, Paul Stewart, Jack Paar

† † †

76. MYSELF WHEN YOUNG

† † † † †

1. From what Broadway show starring Ethel Merman, William Gaxton, and Victor Moore did these tunes come: "You're the Top," "All Through the Night," "I Get a Kick Out of You," and "Blow, Gabriel, Blow"?

* * *

2. From what Broadway show starring Lucienne Boyer did "Hands Across the Table" come?

* * *

3. From what Broadway show starring Libby Holman did "You and the Night and the Music" come?

* * *

4. Who married the sister of The Duke of Wellington, but soared from midshipman to Lord of the Admiralty on his own abilities?

* * *

5. Name two detectives created by Henry Kane.

* * *

6. Who created Nick Carter?

* * *

7. What was the family name of the children in *Peter Pan*?

* * *

8. Who was the American politician fictionalized in John Dos Passos' *Number One*?

* * *

9. Who wrote *This Is War:* a) Stephen Vincent Benet; b) Arch Oboler; or c) Norman Corwin?

*　*　*

10. What product saved you money because it had a Meter Miser?

† † †

77. PINCH-HITTING NAMES

† † † † †

Match the nickname with the baseball player.

1. Slim	a) Ralph Perkins
2. Mike	b) Johnny Mize
3. Red	c) Frank O'Doul
4. Cy	d) Edmund Miller
5. Dode	e) George Paskert
6. Salty	f) Harold Newhouser
7. Lefty	g) Francis Parker
8. Hal	h) Dominic J. Ryba
9. Big Cat	i) Harry F. Sallee
10. Bing	j) Charles Ruffing

† † †

78. THE 'FIFTY-SIX THEATER

† † † † †

Match the star and the show of 1956.

1. *Fallen Angels*
2. *The Diary of Anne Frank*
3. *Waiting for Godot*
4. *Auntie Mame*
5. *Long Day's Journey into Night*
6. *Bells are Ringing*

a) Jason Robards, Jr
b) Nancy Walker
c) Judy Holliday
d) Susan Strasberg
e) Bert Lahr
f) Rosalind Russell

† † †

79. 'FIFTY-SIX VIDEO

† † † † †

Complete the names of these 10 top 1956 TV shows.

1. "Ed ——— Show"

* * *

2. "——— Question"

* * *

3. "The ——— Como Show"

* * *

4. "I ——— Lucy"

* * *

5. "December ———"

* * *

6. "——— Scouts"

* * *

7. You ——— Your Life"

* * *

8. "The Red ——— Show"

* * *

9. "What's ——— Line"

* * *

10. "———land"

† † †

80. 'FIFTY-SIX FLIX

Match the 1956 movie and the star.

1. *Too Bad She's Bad*

2. *Picnic*

3. *Richard III*

4. *The Man in the Gray Flannel Suit*

5. *Bus Stop*

a) Kirk Douglas

b) James Dean

c) Sophia Loren

d) Laurence Olivier

e) Martin and Lewis

6. *Pardners*	f) William Holden
7. *Lust for Life*	g) Gregory Peck
8. *The Last Wagon*	h) Victor Mature
9. *Giant*	i) Richard Widmark
10. *The Shark Fighters*	j) Marilyn Monroe

81. CAST THE MOVIE #3

1. Paul Muni, Marguerite Chapman, Larry Parks and Philip Van Zandt
2. Grace McDonald, Robert Paige, Virginia Dale and Peter Lind Hayes
3. Bette Davis, Franchot Tone, Margaret Lindsay and Alison Skipworth
4. Yvonne de Carlo, Richard Green, Jackie Gleason and Rock Hudson
5. Ginger Rogers, Clifton Webb, Jeffrey Hunter and Anne Francis
6. Paul Douglas, Linda Darnell, Celeste Holm and Charles Coburn
7. Robert Taylor, Ruth Hussey, Walter Pidgeon and Paul Kelly
8. Marlene Dietrich, Charles Boyer, Basil Rathbone and Joseph Schildkraut
9. Rosalind Russell, Melvyn Douglas, Sid Caesar and Nina Foch
10. Lewis Stone, Mickey Rooney, Cecilia Parker and Fay Holden

a) *The Garden of Allah*
b) *Flight Command*
c) *Everybody Does It*
d) *Counter-Attack*

e) *The Hardys Ride High*
f) *Dancing on a Dime*
g) *Dangerous*
h) *The Guilt of Janet Ames*
i) *Dreamboat*
j) *Desert Hawk*

† † †

82. WHO (#1)

† † † † †

1. —— played Peter Gunn's girlfriend; a stripper in *A Cold Wind in August;* Richard Widmark's wife in *The Way West?*

* * *

2. —— played Jimmy Stewart's secretary in *Anatomy of A Murder;* Our Miss Brooks; a Russian hotel maid; Otto Kruger's wisecracking assistant?

* * *

3. —— played Jeanne Crain's sister; a courtesan; a lame poison-pen writer?

* * *

4. —— played Burt Lancaster's ex-wife; Kurt Kasznar's partner; John Wayne's housekeeper?

* * *

5. —— played a banana plantation owner; Arlene Dahl's sister; a Confederate spy?

* * *

6. —— played Walter Pidgeon's daughter; Glenn Ford's wife; Gertrude Lawrence at 12; Dick Powell's fiancee; Honey West?

* * *

7. —— played John Wayne's girlfriend; Preston Foster's daughter; Sterling Hayden's girlfriend; Ronald Reagan's fiancee?

* * *

8. —— played a bookshop clerk; comic strip artist; Robert Stack's widow; Robert Stack's sister?

* * *

9. —— played Cliff Robertson's ex-wife; Edmond O'Brien's wife; an Indian captive; Henry Fonda's wife?

* * *

10. —— played Jo Van Fleet's daughter-in-law; Aldo Ray's wife; Texas Guinan?

† † †

83. MEMORABLE MOTTOES

With whom do you associate the following?

1. "No job too tough, no mystery too baffling."

* * *

2. "Ars Gratia Artis"

* * *

103

3. "AuH$_2$O"

*   *   *

4. "There is no such thing as a bad boy."

*   *   *

5. "My battle against Scorpia represents the battle between good and evil."

*   *   *

6. "In brightest day, in blackest night, no evil shall escape my sight."

*   *   *

7. "That's all, folks!"

*   *   *

8. "Roll, Thunder, roll!"

*   *   *

9. "When the going gets tough, the tough get going."

*   *   *

10. "Period. End of Report."

† † †

84. TV QUIZ QUIZ

† † † † †

Match the TV Quiz Show and the host.

1.	"Answer Yes or No"	a)	Jack Lescouli
2.	"$100,000 Big Surprise"	b)	Bert Parks
3.	"Break the Bank"	c)	Johnny Carson
4.	"It's Your Bet"	d)	Bill Cullen
5.	"Bank on the Stars"	e)	Lyle Waggoner
6.	"Laugh Line"	f)	Fred Allen
7.	"Judge for Yourself"	g)	Moss Hart
8.	"Earn Your Vacation"	h)	Mike Wallace
9.	"Brains and Brawn"	j)	Jack Paar
10.	"Eye Guess"	k)	Merv Griffin
11.	"Snap Judgment"	l)	Ed McMahon
12.	"Play Your Hunch"	m)	Dick Van Dyke

† † †

85. CRITICAL GUESSES, #5

† † † † †

What film is being reviewed?

1. "Miss Hutton, it is perfectly clear, is the closest possible human approximation of a buzz bomb." —*New York Post.*
2. "Isn't the chance of watching Gary Cooper, in a colonial costume and tri-cornered hat, acting the gallant frontiersman sufficient for anyone? If it isn't, there's Paulette Goddard as the red-headed, flashing-eyed slave." —*New York Times.*
3. "Bogart is triumphant. And Mary Astor is better than she has been in a long list of assignments." —*New York Herald-Tribune.*
4. "Brian Donlevy is utterly right as the commanding major." —*New York Herald-Tribune.*
5. "The tragic Sophie, drowning her unendurable grief in Paris bistros, is beautifully realized in Anne Baxter's sensitive portrayal." —*New York Herald-Tribune.*
6. "Alice Faye proves that she is as fine a dramatic actress as she is an entertainer of song and dance, when, as the flashy glamorous Belle, she sweeps across the screen." —*New York Daily News.*
7. "The children are so moving that one is almost apt to overlook the really fine performance of Robert Young." —*New York Times.*
8. "With Robert Walker playing like a veteran trouper, and such excellent supporting performers as Robert Benchley, Keenan Wynn, Ray Collins and Chill Wills adding a wide range of clowning, it is singularly satisfying." —*New York Herald-Tribune.*
9. "Garfield's under-acting keys the production to its central theme, but Eleanor Parker lends invaluable support as the girl Schmid leaves behind him." —*New York Herald-Tribune.*

10. "Spencer Tracy plays Doolittle as only he could do it." —*New York Herald-Tribune*.

a) *Pride of the Marines*
b) *The Razor's Edge*
c) *And the Angels Sing*
c) *Across the Pacific*
e) *Thirty Seconds Over Tokyo*
f) *In Old Chicago*
g) *Unconquered*
h) *A Journey for Margaret*
i) *See Here, Private Hargrove*
j) *Wake Island*

† † †

86. CAREER QUIZ

† † † † †

1. He debuted in *Builder of Bridges* (1915) and was last seen in *Little Women* (1949). His other films included *Trader Horn, Tarzan, the Ape Man, Queen Christina, The House of Rothschild, Curtain at Eight, Lives of A Bengal Lancer, The Crusades,* and *The Four Feathers*.

2. He debuted in *Orphans of the Storm* (1922) and was last seen in *The Greatest Story Ever Told*. (1965). His other films included *King of Kings, Show Boat, Viva Villa, Cleopatra, The Crusades, Slave Ship, The Life of Emile Zola, A Star is Born, Suez,* and *Idiot's Delight*.

3. He was first seen in 1921's *The Gilded Lily* and last seen in 1961's *Wild in the Country*. In between he appeared in *The Heart of Maryland, Lightnin, Abraham Lincoln, Salvation Nell, Broadway Bill, The President Vanished, The Crusades, The White Legion, Seven Keys to Baldpate* and *Fighting Father Dunne*.

4. He spanned the years from 1915's *Great While It Lasted* to 1962's *Pocketful of Miracles*. He also appeared in *Arizona Days, Perils of Pauline, Blackmail, A Man of a Thousand Faces* and *Studs Lonigan*.

5. In 1911 he was in *The Papered Door* and in 1967 in *Gunn*. He was also in *Crime Doctor, Dust Be My Destiny, Meet Boston Blackie, The Glass Key, Lassie Come Home, The Wild One* and *Invasion of the Body Snatchers*.

6. He was in 1917's *Modern Cinderella* and 1950's *Key to the City*. He was also in *The Great Ziegfeld, Saratoga, Rosalie, Sweethearts, The Wizard of Oz, The Shop Around the Corner, The Mortal Storm, Tortilla Flat* and *Casanova Brown*.

7. In 1915 he was in *Chimmie Fadden* and in 1955 he was in *The Seven Year Itch*. He also appeared in *Swing Time, Gold Diggers of 1937, Louisiana Purchase, Duffy's Tavern* and *Ziegfeld Follies*.

8. In 1917 she debuted in *The Little Princess* and she closed out her career in 1963 in *It's a Mad, Mad, Mad, Mad World*. She also appeared in *Souls for Sale, The Wedding March, No, No, Nanette, The Guardsman, Penrod and Sam, Destry Rides Again, Westward Passage, Back Street, Dames, Ruggles of Red Gap*, and *Life with Father*.

9. She was in *Man's Genesis* (1912) and in *Arabella* (1968). In between she was in *Judith of Bethulia, The Birth of a Nation, Intolerance, Rebecca of Sunnybrook Farm, Tales of Manhattan, Jane Eyre, A Tree Grows in Brooklyn, Apartment for Peggy, The Snake Pit, The Robe*, and *From the Terrace*.

10. In 1917 he was in *The Spreading Dawn* and in 1960 he appeared in *Heller in Pink Tights*. And along the way he was featured in *Easy Lynne, East of Suez, What Price Glory, In Old Arizona, Dinner at Eight, Dillinger, Good Sam* and *The Last Hurrah*.

a) Joseph Schildkraut
b) Mae Marsh
c) Frank Morgan
d) Jason Robards Sr.
e) Edmund Lowe
f) Victor Moore

g) Harry "Snub" Pollard
h) C. Aubrey Smith
i) ZaSu Pitts
j) Pat O'Malley

† † †

87. NOM DE BAT

† † † † †

Match the baseball monicker with the real name.

1. Heinie   a) Al Schoendienst

2. Ozark Ike   b) Henry Zimmerman

3. Zeke   c) Henry W. Wyse

4. Hooks   d) John A. Schmitz

5. Gus   e) Gus E. Zernial

6. Buckshot   f) Herman A. Schaefer

7. Red   g) Raymond W. Schalk

8. Bear Tracks   h) Allen L. Zarilla

9. Cracker   i) Early Wynn

10. Germany   j) Forest G. Wright

† † †

✝ ✝ ✝ ✝ ✝

ACROSS

1. Empties (7).
5. Hitchcock film (7).
9. Lillian Smith book, Billie Holiday song, "— Fruit" (7).
10. Star of *I'm All Right Jack* (7).
12. *McGuffey's* — (6).
14. Moxie (8).
17. Yale teams (8).
18. Marxist humor (6).
21. Old Pete (6, 9)
24. What Mrs. Peel and Mr. Steed did (6).
25. Redistricted (7).
26. Emptied (7).
27. Houdini's stock in trade (7).

DOWN

1. It came from Mars, said Welles (7).
2. 21A threw a good one (5, 4).
3. Lone Ranger's faithful companion (5).
4. Rustler's targets (4).
5. Silent films today badly need one (8).
6. "The Colgate Sports Newsreel" starred him (4, 5).
7. "You're the ——— in My Coffee" (5).
8. State of being away (7).
13. Former New York State boxing commissioner (5, 4).
15. During the Depression there was an ——— of unemployed (9).
16. Lewis Stone: "You're a gran' son." Mickey Rooney: "And you're ———" (1, 7).
17. Swing music ensemble (3, 4).
19. Denunciations (7).
20. *Our* ——— *Were Young and Gay* (6).
22. Soap ———. (5).
23. Soldiers from Down Under (5).

✝ ✝ ✝

110

Quiz-Word No. 7

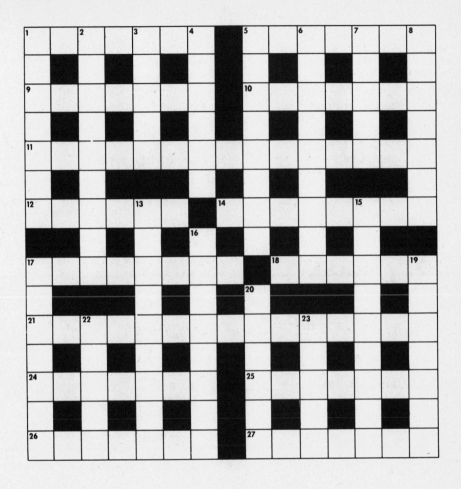

88. MATCH MATES

✝ ✝ ✝ ✝ ✝

Match wife with husband.

1. Wallace Beery	a) Ethel Merman
2. Ernest Borgnine	b) Patricia Medina
3. Jackie Coogan	c) Gloria Swanson
4. Joseph Cotten	d) Barbara Stanwyck
5. Robert Taylor	e) Betty Grable

✝ ✝ ✝

89. VERSATILE VINCENT

✝ ✝ ✝ ✝ ✝

Match the Vincent Price character with the movie.

1. *Brigham Young*	a) Boss Tweed
2. *Hudson's Bay*	b) William G. McAdoo
3. *Tower of London*	c) Prince Prospero
4. *Wilson*	d) Joseph Smith
5. *Laura*	e) King Charles II
6. *Dragonwyck*	f) James Addison Reavis
7. *Up in Central Park*	g) Nicholas Medina
8. *The Baron of Arizona*	h) Duke Clarence
9. *The Raven*	i) Shelby Carpenter
10. *The Pit and the Pendulum*	j) Dr. Craven
11. *The Masque of the Red Death*	k) Van Ryn

✝ ✝ ✝

90. FAMOUS PEOPLE

† † † † †

1. Arlene Francis was the hostess of TV's "Blind Date." Can you name her famous actor-husband?

* * *

2. Who was the newscaster who said good night with these words, "Glad we could get together."?

* * *

3. What song did the grandfather on "My Three Sons" introduce in vaudeville?

* * *

4. Who was "The Cheerful Little Earful"?

* * *

5. Who was "The Tune Detective"?

* * *

6. When Lord Charles Cavendish married, what act broke up?

* * *

7. Which national figure received a hike in pay in 1949 from $25,000 to $100,000 a year?

* * *

8. Who was Steve Early?

* * *

113

9. Who was Gov. Fielding Wright's running mate on the States Rights ticket, 1948?

* * *

10. Robert Burns came North after doing what?

† † †

91. BROADCAST BACKLIST

† † † † †

Match the radio show, the actors and the creator.

1. "Abie's Irish Rose"	a) Roland Young, Paul Mann, Frances Chaney	I. Thorne Smith
2. "The Adventures of Huckleberry Finn"	b) Gerald Mohr	II. Anne Nichols
3. "The Adventures of M. Hercule Poirot"	c) Ezra Stone, House Jameson, Lea Penman, Betty Field	III. Raymond Chandler
4. "The Adventures of Nero Wolfe"	d) Richard Bond, Mercedes McCambridge	IV. Clifford Goldsmith
5. "The Adventures of Philip Marlow"	e) Harold Huber	V. George McManus
6. "The Adventures of Topper"	f) Neil O'Malley, Agnes Moorehead	VI. Agatha Christie
7. "The Aldrich Family"	g) Jack Grimes, Maurice Ellis	VII. Rex Stout
8. "Bringing Up Father"	h) Santos Ortega, Louis Vitte	VIII. Mark Twain

† † †

92. SCREENPLAY PEOPLE

† † † † †

Match the movie, the director, and the description.

1. *Maytime in Mayfair*	a)	George Seaton
2. *Mutiny*	b)	Gregory La Cava
3. *Northwest Passage*	c)	John Farrow
4. *One Way Passage*	d)	George Sidney
5. *Page Miss Glory*	e)	Herbert Wilcox
6. *Park Row*	f)	Edward Dmytryk
7. *Junior Miss*	g)	King Vidor
8. *Affairs of Cellini*	h)	Tay Garnett
9. *The Big Clock*	i)	Mervyn LeRoy
10. *Cass Timberlane*	j)	Samuel Fuller

I.   Anna Neagle and Michael Wilding as denizens of London's plushest district.

II. Mark Stevens fights the British during the War of 1812.

III. Newspapers as they were published in New York during the 19th Century.

IV. Ray Milland and Charles Laughton in a big magazine murder mystery.

V.   Fredric March and Constance Bennett get a chance to wear Renaissance garb.

VI. Marion Davies is accidentally chosen a beauty contest winner.

VII. Kay Francis and William Powell light cigarettes during a toast to what might have been.

VIII. Spencer Tracy in Sinclair Lewis' novel.

IX. Peggy Ann Garner and Allyn Joslyn play daughter and father.

X.   Spencer Tracy in frontier garb.

† † †

93. CAPTAIN ON THE BRIDGE

† † † † †

Match the captain, his ship, and the place where they both appear.

1. Nelson
2. Ahab
3. Edward Vere
4. Andy Hawks
5. Jacobi
6. Adam Troy
7. Christopher Pike
8. Thiele
9. Englehorn
10. Richard Richard-
    son
11. Nemo
12. Larson
13. Kinross
14. Grey Holden
15. Flint

   a) "Enterprise"
   b) "Tiki"
   c) "Nerka"
   d) "La Paloma"
   e) "Nautilus"
   f) "Walrus"
   g) "Indomitable"
   h) "Seaview"
   i) "Pequod"
   j) "Cotton Blossom"
   k) "Venture"
   l) "Vera"
   m) "Ghost"
   n) "Torrin"

I. *Run Silent, Run Deep*
II. *In Which We Serve*
III. *Moby Dick*
IV. "Adventures in Paradise"
V. *Show Boat*
VI. "Riverboat"
VII. *The Maltese Falcon*
VIII. *Ship of Fools*
IX. "Voyage to the Bottom of The Sea"
X. *Billy Budd*
XI. "Star Trek"
XII. *Treasure Island*
XIII. *The Sea Wolf*
XIV. *King Kong*
XV. *Twenty Thousand Leagues Under The Sea*

† † †

94.   SPORTING GROWD

1.   Dark Star beat what horse in the 1953 Kentucky Derby?

* * *

2.   Who were "The Hitless Wonders"?

* * *

3.   Who was Edward Carl Gaedel?

* * *

4.   Who was the famous football coach at Carlisle?

* * *

5.   Who's missing from the Philadelphia A's $100,000 infield: John Phalen McInnis, Edward Trowbridge Collins, John Franklin Baker?

* * *

6.   What was Equipoise's nickname?

* * *

7.   Swaps set a world record of 1:33-$\frac{1}{5}$ on June 9, 1956 at which track?

* * *

8.   Which football team wore basketball shoes in the 1934 championship contest?

* * *

9. Who were the Steagles?

* * *

10. What did Mark Christman, Nelson Potter, Jack Kramer, Gene Moore, Milt Byrnes, Don Gutteridge, Franck Mancuso, Sig Jakuck, George McQuinn, George Caster, Mike Kreevich and Chet Laabs have in common?

† † †

95. CRITICAL GUESSES, #6

What film is being reviewed?

1. "John Carradine as the vicious Heydrich is excellent." —*New York Herald-Tribune.*
2. "Possibly because she is the best-realized character in the book, Pilar dominates the film." —*Newsweek.*
3. "The great thing which Mr. Coward has accomplished in this film is a full and complete expression of national fortitude." —*New York Times.*
4. "It is distinguished by 1) a moving love story, 2) the unveiling of Miss Garson's interesting legs." —*Time.*
5. "It's an old device—but a good one—the substitution of identical twins—which Metro has used as the main twist." —*New York Times.*
6. "Darryl Zanuck, hiding behind his favorite pseudonym (Melville Crossman), has written a plausible and shocking story." —*Newsweek.*
7. "A little slimmer than in her past screen appearances, and with considerable more confidence, the blonde figure skater impresses for the first time as an actress." —*Newsweek.*
8. "Miss Merman rallies round to keep the score going when Miss Faye drops in her soundtrack." —*New York Times.*
9. "Miss Crain brings proper dignity and sincerity to her role, although she's not always convincing and is frequently over-

shadowed in the thespic department by such vets as Miss Barrymore and Miss Waters." —*Variety*.

10. "Grant plays the submarine captain with his customary quizzical forcefulness." —*New York Herald-Tribune*.

a) *Nazi Agent*
b) *For Whom The Bell Tolls*
c) *Pinky*
d) *Random Harvest*
e) *Hitler's Madman*
f) *Alexander's Ragtime Band*
g) *The Purple Heart*
h) *In Which We Serve*
i) *Destination Tokyo*
j) *Sun Valley Serenade*

† † †

96. QUIET ON THE SET!

Match the movie, the director and the description.

1. *It's Always Fair Weather*
2. *The Kid from Brooklyn*
3. *Kitty Foyle*
4. *Lady of Burlesque*
5. *Lawyer Man*
6. *The Little Foxes*
7. *The Long Gray Line*
8. *Macao*
9. *Made for Each Other*
10. *The Marrying Kind*

a) John Cromwell
b) George Cukor
c) William Dieterle
d) William Wyler
e) Josef von Sternberg
f) Sam Wood
g) Norman Z. McLeod
h) Gene Kelly
i) William Wellman
j) John Ford

I. Bill Powell and Joan Blondell and the mobs.
II. Judy Holliday and Aldo Ray, about to split, recall their marriage.
III. Jane Russell in love with Robert Mitchum.
IV. Three vets find their 10th reunion to be bittersweet.
V. A milkman becomes a prizefighter.

VI. Ginger Rogers as a working class heroine.
VII. Barbara Stanwyck solves murders.
VIII. Betty Davis plays Regina.
IX. Tyrone Power, Maureen O'Hara, shamrocks and the Point.
X. Carole Lombard and James Stewart are newlyweds.

† † †

97. CREATIVE COMICS

Name the cartoon creator of:

1. Judge Puzzle

* * *

2. Pete the Tramp

* * *

3. Sentinel Louie

* * *

4. Aunt Eppie Hogg

* * *

5. Rosie's Beau

* * *

6. Wash Tubbs

* * *

7. The Phantom

* * *

8. Cap Stubbs

† † †

98. WITHOUT PROMPTING

† † † † †

1. Who wrote the score for "Victory at Sea"?

* * *

2. Who was the ugliest woman in Lower Slobbovia?

* * *

3. What was Lai Choi San's nickname?

* * *

4. Who were Reed Richards, Johnny Storm, Ben Grimm and Sue Masters?

* * *

5. Who invented the phrases: a) "The Forgotten Man," and b) "New Deal"?

* * *

6. What do Grovers Mills, N.J., and Horsell Common, Surrey, have in common?

* * *

7. From what Broadway show did "The Last Round-up", "Wagon Wheels" and "The House is Haunted" come from?

* * *

8. Who coined the term, "The Jazz Age"?

*   *   *

9. Who were the pets in Sheila Burnford's *The Incredible Journey?*

*   *   *

10. Robert Sherwood's play, *There Shall Be No Night*, was about: a) The Russo-Finnish War; b) a blinded veteran; c) The Sacco-Vanzetti trial?

†   †   †

99. THOSE GREAT RADIO PROGRAMS

†   †   †   †   †

1. Buck Rogers sent you a solar scout badge if you mailed a boxtop from what cereal . . . a planetary map if you sent in a strip from what can?

*   *   *

2. Who sponsored "Frank Crummit and Julia Sanderson"?

*   *   *

3. Who sponsored "The Moylan Sisters"?

*   *   *

4. Who sponsored "Dr. IQ"?

*   *   *

5. Who sponsored "Silver Theatre"?

*   *   *

6. Who was the radio orchestra leader known as "The Evangelist of Rhythm"?

*   *   *

7. Who starred on "Sweeney and March"?

*   *   *

8. What radio comedy was based on Russ Westover's comic strip?

*   *   *

9. Ellen Brown ran a tea room in Simpsonville on what serial?

*   *   *

10. John L. C. Sivoney (Frank Fontaine) was heard on what radio show?

†   †   †

ACROSS

1. English for *the dansant* (3, 5).
5. Stabbed (6).
10. What we had to do after 1929 (9).
11. Janet (5).
12. Dawes, Garner, Truman, Barkley (5).
13. Schoolyard sport (3, 3, 3).
17. Movie theatre impresario S. L. Rothafel (4).
19. The Sheik was one (4).
20. Nonsense! (10).
22. Nostalgia time (9).
24. "Call Me ———" (5).
26. Popeye's girl (5).
27. Upper Crusts (5, 4).
28. Hark, who cometh? (2, 6)

DOWN

1. First big radio variety show, 1923 (3, 8, 4).
2. Book by Commander Richard Byrd (5).
3. Early phonograph record (8).
4. Leonard Marx (5).
6. Italian aeronaut who flew over the Pole in 1928 (6).
7. He starred in *A Hatful of Rain* (9).
8. She married Sinclair Lewis (7, 8).
9. James Dean did this in the Nicholas Ray film of 1955 (8).
14. Lively sphere.
15. Once popular rugs and posing grounds for birthday suit wearers (9).
16. Coax (8).
18. Vividly expressive (8).
21. End of a long dry spell (6).
23. Nostalgiacs ——— for the good old days (5).

Quiz-Word No. 8

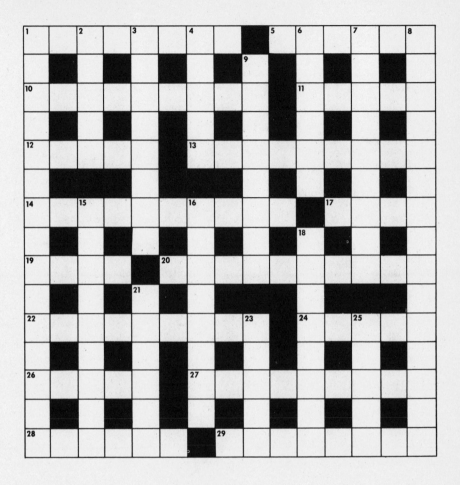

100. DRINK UP

† † † † †

Match the saloon with the movie or TV show.

1. Admiral Benbow
2. Blue Parrot Cafe
3. Butch's Bar
4. Rick's Cafe Americaine
5. Long Branch
6. Gerard's Cafe
7. Dino's
8. Charleston Club

a) "77 Sunset Strip"
b) *Casablanca*
c) "Gunsmoke"
d) *Treasure Island*
e) "The Roaring Twenties"
f) *To Have and Have Not*
g) *The Best Years of Our Lives*

† † †

101. REMINISCING

1. Who practiced law in Maycomb, Alabama?

        *   *   *

2. Ingrid Bergman and Cary Grant engage in a very long kiss in what Hitchcock film?

        *   *   *

3. Mark Hellinger produced *The Naked City*. Who directed it?

        *   *   *

4. Who rode Tony?

        *   *   *

5. What was the name of the horse Roddy McDowall loved? The name of the horse Elizabeth Taylor loved?

        *   *   *

6. Spencer Tracy and Hedy Lamarr starred in the movie version of what Steinbeck book?

        *   *   *

7. Sonia is a duck in which Walt Disney picture?

        *   *   *

8. Who plays John Baron in *Suddenly*?

        *   *   *

9. Van Heflin, Jean Arthur and Alan Ladd starred in what western?

        *   *   *

10.   Who rode Diablo?

$$* \quad * \quad *$$

11.   In what movie does Charles Laughton play a butler?

$$* \quad * \quad *$$

12.   What was the newsreel feature produced by Fox?

$$\dagger \quad \dagger \quad \dagger$$

102. COMPETITION

† † † † †

1. The Chicago Bears totaled what team in the 1940 NFL title meet (score, 73-0)?

* * *

2. In 1955, Nashua won a) 150,000; b) $257,000; c) $525,750; or d) $752,550.

* * *

3. Who won the 1943 Kentucky Derby, Belmont Stakes and Preakness?

* * *

4. What horse beat Swaps in the 1955 Washington Park match race?

* * *

5. What year was the Soap Box Derby first held: a) 1924; b) 1934; or c) 1944?

* * *

6. Who was the first swimmer to cross the English Channel using the crawl?

* * *

7. The Staley Athletic Club of Decatur became what football team in 1922?

* * *

8. What team did the Chicago Bears play inside Chicago Stadium, December, 1932, to decide the NFL championship?

* * *

9. What was the Wesleyan-Yale game of 1906 noted for?

* * *

10. Who rode these Kentucky Derby winners: Lawrin, Whirlaway, Hoop, Jr., Citation and Hill Gail?

† † †

103. INDELIBLE FACTS

† † † † †

1. "On the Banks of the Wabash" was written by Paul Dresser, Theodore Dreiser's brother. In what W. C. Fields' movie is this song heard?

* * *

2. Name two songs sung by Dooley Wilson in *Casablanca*.

* * *

3. Hal Roach Studios was responsible for what kid series?

* * *

4. What did Charles Laughton and Trevor Howard have in common?

* * *

5. Who wrote the original novel that *Ben Hur* was based on? What Army rank did he hold?

* * *

6. Who plays Ilsa Lund Laszlo in *Casablanca*?

* * *

7. Mabel Normand worked for which great comedy director?

* * *

8. What subject did Mr. Chips teach?

* * *

9. *Plunder* and *The Black Secret* featured what serial performer?

*   *   *

10. What did Fredric March, King Baggot, John Barrymore and Spencer Tracy all have in common?

† † †

104. BASIL RATHBONE

† † † † †

Match the Basil Rathbone role with the movie.

1. *David Copperfield*   a) Sir Guy of Gisbourne

2. *Captain Blood*   b) Andre Trochard

3. *The Last Days of Pompeii*   c) Murdstone

4. *A Tale of Two Cities*   d) Pontius Pilate

5. *Romeo and Juliet*   e) Talbalt

6. *Tovarich*   f) Louis XI

7. *The Adventures of
Robin Hood*   g) Norman Case

8. *If I Were King*   h) Captain Levasseur

9. *My Three Angels*   i) Marquis d'Evremonde

10. *The Last Hurrah*   j) Commissar Gorotchenko

† † †

105. CAR ADS

† † † † †

Name the car that used the advertising slogan. . . .

1. "Hitch your braggin' to this star"

* * *

2. "Strength, safety, style and speed"

* * *

3. "Just a real good car"

* * *

4. "Somewhere West of Laramie"

* * *

5. "The car of the year in eye appeal and buy appeal"

* * *

6. "Ask the man who owns one"

* * *

7. "Sets the style"

* * *

8. "Beauty beyond belief"

† † †

106. BROUGHT TO YOU BY

† † † † †

Match the sponsor and the radio show.

1. Ivory Soap   a) "Kaltenborn Edits the News"

2. Pabst   b) "Ma Perkins"

3. Chase and Sanborn   c) "Life Can Be Beautiful"

4. Pure Oil Co.   d) "Edgar Bergen and Charlie McCarthy"

5. Oxydol   e) "Little Orphan Annie"

6. Ovaltine   f) "The Right to Happiness"

7. Camay   g) "Pepper Young's Family"

8. Spic and Span   h) "The Danny Kaye Show"

† † †

107. REAL NAMES, #1

† † † † †

Match the pseudonym and the real name.

1. Bert Lahr a) Odessa Cowan
2. Dorothy Lamour b) Merwyn Bogue
3. Frances Langford c) Elizabeth Edith Enke
4. Peggy Lee d) Gladys Greene
5. Ted Lewis e) Anna Myrtle Swoyer
6. Ina Ray Hutton f) Irving Lahrheim
7. Ish Kabibble g) Theodore Leopold Friedman
8. Edie Adams h) Dorothy Stanton
9. Jean Arthur i) Norma Jean Egstrom
10. Nancy Walker j) Frances Newbern

† † †

108. DIVERSE DAVID

† † † † †

Match the David Niven role with the movie.

1. *The Charge of the Light Brigade*   a) Aaron Burr

2. *The Prisoner of Zenda*   b) Sir Arthur Robertson

3. *Wuthering Heights*   c) Captain Randall

4. *The Magnificent Doll*   d) Edgar Linton

5. *Separate Tables*   f) Fritz von Tarlenheim

6. *Fifty-Five Days at Peking*   e) Major Pollock

† † †

109. SPORTING TYPES

† † † † †

1. Who rode all of these Kentucky Derby winners: Zev, Flying Ebony, Gallant Fox?

* * *

2. Which NFL player competed in the most championship games?

* * *

3. Who was the ball player (.258 batting average in 488 games) who became an evangelist?

* * *

4. Who started Little League Baseball?

* * *

5. Who invented miniature golf?

* * *

6. Whose sports column was called "The Sportlight"?

* * *

7. Who bought Man O'War from August Belmont for $5,000?

* * *

8. Who was the Cleveland quarterback who distinguished himself in the Cleveland-Detroit 1954 NFL title contest?

* * *

9. Who wore #78 for the Cleveland Browns?

*   *   *

10. Who scored the only touchdown in the Harvard-Center College (Danville, Ky.) 1921 game, when Center won 6-0?

† † †

110. WHO, TWO

† † † † †

1. Who was the movie star (*The Love of Sunya*, *The Desert Song*), who had been an American spy during the First World War?
2. Who was known as "The Handcuff King"?
3. Who was known as "Froggie" and worked with Fred Waring?
4. Who appeared in every DeMille film after the coming of talkies?
5. Who was the governor impeached in 1923?
6. Who was known as "The Mary Pickford of France"?
7. Who impersonated Field Marshal Montgomery during World War II?
8. Whose career was hampered because he resembled Clark Gable?
9. Who played "Schlepperman" on "The Jack Benny Show"?
10. Who was known as "The Silver King of the Cowboys"?

a) Clifton James
b) Maude Fealy
c) John Boles
d) Weldon Heyburn
e) Jack Walton
f) George Brindmour
g) Sam Hearn
h) Susanne Grandais
i) Walter J. Froes
j) Gene Gray

† † †

111. DOCUMENTARY DIRECTORS

† † † † †

Who directed these World War II films?

1. *Memphis Belle*
2. *Fighting Lady*
3. *San Pietro*
4. *The Battle of Midway*
5. *Marines on Tarawa*

a) John Ford
b) Leland Hayward
c) William Wyler
d) Louis De Rochemont
e) John Huston

† † †

112. FLASHBACKS

1. What was the Landis-Eastman Line of 1943?

       *   *   *

2. Out of which stable did Citation come?

       *   *   *

3. Who was the first President to have a phone on his desk?

       *   *   *

4. Major Dwight D. Eisenhower in 1932 earned how much a year: a) $3,000; b) $5,000; or c) $10,000?

       *   *   *

5. Who was Juan de la Cierva?

       *   *   *

6. What were "Byrne-outs"?

       *   *   *

7. What were "pony editions"?

       *   *   *

8. What was the "John Fitch"?

       *   *   *

9. What did Paul Revere, Axis Sally and Tokyo Rose have in common?

*   *   *

10. What was the "Jacob Jones"?

† † †

113. FROM A BOOK BY

† † † † †

1. Who wrote the play *Command Decision?*
2. Who wrote the novel *Stella Dallas?*
3. Who wrote the novel *Ramona?*
4. Who wrote the novel *Untamed?*
5. Who wrote the story "Hallelujah, I'm a Bum"?
6. Who wrote the story "The Purple Heart"?
7. Who wrote the novel *Arch of Triumph?*
8. Who wrote the novel *Kitty Foyle?*
9. Who wrote the novel *One More Spring?*
10. Who wrote the play *Seventh Heaven?*

a) Robert Nathan
b) Melville Crossman
c) Helen Hunt Jackson
d) Austin Strong
e) Erich Maria Remarque
f) Helga Moray
g) William Wister Haines
h) Christopher Morley
i) Ben Hecht
j) Olive Higgins Prouty

† † †

114. MOVIE MAYHEM

† † † † †

1. Who directed *Pick-up on South Street* and *House of Bamboo?*
2. Who played the lead in *Roger Touhy, Gangster?*
3. Who directed *Confessions of Boston Blackie, Murder My Sweet* and *Crossfire?*
4. Who was the crooked private eye in *The Asphalt Jungle?*
5. Who played George Raft in *The George Raft Story?*
6. Who played the Crime Reporter in the "Crime Does Not Pay" series?
7. Who was the first Sam Spade?
8. Who wrote the original novels that these films were based on: *The Falcoln Takes Over, Murder My Sweet, The Big Sleep, The Brasher Doubloon?*
9. Who helps Edward G. Robinson out in *The Whole Town's Talking?*
10. Who played "Sugarpuss" O'Shea in *Ball of Fire?*

a) Preston Foster
b) Raymond Chandler
c) Edward Dmytryk
d) Reed Hadley
e) Brad Dexter
f) Jean Arthur
g) Samuel Fuller
h) Barbara Stanwyck
i) Ray Danton
j) Ricardo Cortez

† † †

145

115. REAL NAMES, #2

✝ ✝ ✝ ✝ ✝

Match the pseudonym and the real name.

1. Janet Blair   a) Joan Brodel
2. Harold Arlen   b) Salvatore Massaro
3. Jimmy Van Heusen   c) Natasha Gurdin
4. Mike Connors   d) Elizabeth June Thornburg
5. Douglas Fairbanks   e) Zelma Hedrick
6. Natalie Wood   f) Krekor Ohanian
7. Betty Hutton   g) Martha Janet Lafferty
8. Kathryn Grayson   h) Julius Ullman
9. Joan Leslie   i) Hyman Arluck
10. Eddie Lang   j) Edward C. Babcock

✝ ✝ ✝

146

116. 'TWENTY-FIVE PICTURE-SHOW

† † † † †

Match the 1925 film with the stars.

1. *So Big*
2. *East of Suez*
3. *Lights of Old Broadway*
4. *Air Mail*
5. *Old Clothes*
6. *Code of the West*
7. *Clothes Make the Pirate*
8. *The Rainbow Trail*
9. *Don Q, Son of Zorro*
10. *Tracked in the Snow Country*
11. *Sally of the Sawdust*
12. *Little Annie Rooney*
13. *The King on Main Street*

a) Marion Davies
b) Jackie Coogan
c) Leon Errol
d) Mary Astor, Douglas Fairbanks
e) W. C. Fields
f) Adolphe Menjou
g) Colleen Moore, Ben Lyon, Phyllis Haver
h) Pola Negri, Edmund Lowe, Rockcliffe Fellowes
i) Billie Dove, Warner Baxter, Douglas Fairbanks, Jr.
i) Constance Bennet, Owen Moore
j) Tom Mix
k) Rin-Tin-Tin
l) Mary Pickford

† † †

117. THE 'TWENTY-FIVE STAGE

† † † † †

Match the stars and the title of these 1925 plays.

1. *They Knew What They Wanted*
2. *Grounds for Divorce*
3. *Cradle Snatchers*
4. *Quarantine*
5. *Outside Looking In*
6. *The Guardsman*
7. *The Vortex*
8. *Candida*
9. *The Jazz Singer*
10. *Big Boy*
11. *Sunny*
12. *Ziegfeld Follies*
13. *Hamlet*
14. *Caesar and Cleopatra*
15. *The Fountain*
16. *Trelawney of the Wells*
17. *The Enchanted April*
18. *The Fall of Eve*

a) Helen Gahagan
b) Walter Huston
c) John Hampden and Ethel Barrymore
d) Marilyn Miller and Clifton Webb
e) George Jessel
f) Noel Coward
g) James Cagney and Charles Bickford
h) Mary Boland and Humphrey Bogart
i) Pauline Lord
j) Ina Claire
k) Helen Hayes
l) Alfred Lunt and Lynn Fontane
m) Katharine Cornell
n) Al Jolson
o) W.C. Fields and Will Rogers
p) Lionel Atwill
p) John Drew and Laurette Taylor
q) Ruth Gordon

† † †

118. HOLLYWOOD HOMICIDE

† † † † †

1. Who played Joe Lilac in *Ball of Fire?*
2. Who directed *The Garment Jungle?*
3. Who wrote the music for *San Quentin, Laura, Lady Without a Passport?*
4. Who played Joel McCrea's girl in *City Streets?*
5. Who played the card hustler strangled in *Dark City?*
6. Who wrote the scores for *Notorious, The Spiral Staircase, Mr. Lucky* and *Crossfire?*
7. Who worked on the screenplays for *Double Indemnity, And Now Tomorrow, The Unseen, The Blue Dahlia* and *Stranger on the Train?*
8. Who played the old Mafia don in *The Brotherhood?*
9. Who had a duplicate accelerator in the back seat of his car in *The Chase?*
10. Who played Johnny Friendly in *On the Waterfront?*

a) Lee J. Cobb
b) Raymond Chandler
c) Sylvia Sidney
d) Dana Andrews
e) Edouard Ciannelli
f) Ed Begley
g) Robert Aldrich
h) Steve Cochran
i) Roy Webb
j) David Raksin

† † †

119.   FLEETING FAME

† † † † †

1.   Who was married to Evelyn Marjorie Baldwin and Linda Arvidson, and appeared in *Rescued from an Eagle's Nest* and *When Knighthood Was in Flower*?

* * *

2.   Whose band was known as "The Cactus Cowboys"?

* * *

3.   Who played Mrs. Hudson in *Hound of the Baskervilles, Adventures of Sherlock Holmes* and *Sherlock Holmes and The Voice of Terror*?

* * *

4.   Who was the first film star to form her own picture company?

* * *

5.   Who was Trixie Friganza's sister?

* * *

6.   Who played Dr. Watson to Arthur Wunter's Holmes?

* * *

7.   Who was nominated for an Oscar for Best Supporting Actress in 1950 (for *Caged*)?

* * *

8.   Who was the burlesque queen ("The Girl With The Million Dollar Legs") who appeared in *The Crown of Lies, Flower of Night* and *The Famous Mrs. Fair*?

* * *

9. Whose two Oscar nominations in 1938 forced the Motion Picture Academy to change the rules?

*   *   *

10. Who won an Oscar for his Best Supporting Role in *The More the Merrier?*

† † †

120.   MEMOIRS

† † † † †

1.   How many blacks were U.S. Army officers in 1940: a) 2; b) 20; c) 200; or d) 2,000?

*   *   *

2.   What did the Kawasaki, Nakajima B5N1 and Mitsubishi G4M1 have in common?

*   *   *

3.   In 1941, how long did it take to fly from New York to Europe: a) 10 hours; b) 20 hours; c) 26½ hours; or d) 53 hours?

*   *   *

4.   Who was Medworth?

*   *   *

5.   Give the nickname for each of these warplanes: a) B-17, b) B-18, c) B-24, d) B-25, e) B-26.

*   *   *

6.   Who flew from Roosevelt Field to Le Bourget Air Field in 33 hours, 39 minutes?

*   *   *

7.   What came to an end on August 10, 1966, after 190 years?

*   *   *

8.   What was the better-known name of World War II spy Elyesa Bazna?

*   *   *

9. What was "Bock's Car"?

*   *   *

10. What did Herman, Arthur, Lloyd and Freddie ("Dock") have in common?

✝   ✝   ✝

153

121. ACADEMY ALSO-RANS

† † † † †

Who was nominated for an Oscar, but failed to get one for work in:

1.	*The Circus*	a)	Frank Morgan
2.	*Thunderbolt*	b)	Bette Davis
3.	*The Big House*	c)	Jean Arthur
4.	*Skippy*	d)	Clark Gable
5.	*The Guardsman*	e)	Jackie Cooper
6.	*Affairs of Cellini*	f)	Wallace Beery
7.	*Mutiny on The Bounty*	g)	George Bancroft
8.	*Mr. Deeds Goes To Town*	h)	Joan Crawford
9.	*Conquest*	i)	Leslie Caron
10.	*Angels With Dirty Faces*	j)	Jeanne Crain
11.	*The Letter*	k)	Alfred Lunt
12.	*The More the Merrier*	l)	Gary Cooper
13.	*Since You Went Away*	m)	Charles Boyer
14.	*The Bells of St. Mary's*	n)	James Cagney
15.	*Brief Encounter*	o)	Ingrid Bergman
16.	*Possessed*	p)	Celia Johnson
17.	*Pinky*	q)	Anne Baxter
18.	*All About Eve*	r)	Deborah Kerr
19.	*Lili*	s)	Charles Chaplin
20.	*Heaven Knows, Mr. Allison*	t)	Claudette Colbert

† † †

122. SCORECARD

1. On June 3, 1932, Giant manager John McGraw resigned. What else happened this day?

* * *

2. Who was the only Canadian ever to manage big league teams?

* * *

3. Who made the longest throw ever recorded for a baseball—445 feet, 10 inches?

* * *

4. Who struck out Tony Lazzeri with loaded bases in the seventh game of the 1926 World Series?

* * *

5. Who is considered the greatest White Sox player of all times?

* * *

6. Who played more games than any other Chicago Cub?

* * *

7. Who was the pitcher the Dodgers sent to a psychiatrist to help him control his wild ball?

* * *

8. Who was known as "the player who could speak nine languages and couldn't hit a curve ball in any of them"?

* * *

155

9. Who specialized in umpire baiting: offering a Coke to the umpire, sending a batboy to play third base, and lying down on the field?

$$* \quad * \quad *$$

10. Who pitched Bobby Thomson the ball that gave the Giants the pennant in 1951?

$$* \quad * \quad *$$

11. Who invented shin guards for catchers?

$$* \quad * \quad *$$

12. Who was the Yankee shortstop who later became a cardiologist?

$$\dagger \quad \dagger \quad \dagger$$

123. CRITICAL GUESSES, #7

† † † † †

What film is being reviewed by the New York Times?

1. "Lionel Belmore gives an easy performance as the town burgomaster. Miss Clarke, Edward Van Sloan and Dwight Frye also serve well."

2. "Miss Crawford is splendid as Flaemmchen. Then there is John Barrymore as the Baron. Nobody could hope to see such a type better acted."

3. "The role of Captain Flagg is played by Victor McLaglen, who is thoroughly in his element."

4. "Lionel Barrymore's Grandpa is the least bit of a let-down after Henry Travers' playing of the role on Broadway."

5. "Claude Rains, as the senior senator, Edward Arnold, as the party steam-roller, Thomas Mitchell, as a roguish correspondent, are splendid all."

6. "William Wyler has directed it magnificently, charging even his lighter scenes with an atmosphere of suspense and foreboding."

7. "Frank Craven as the druggist and narrator is the perfect New England Socrates—honest, sincere, and profound. Martha Scott, as the young girl, is lovely and vibrant with emotion, and William Holden plays the boy with a clean and refreshing youthfulness."

8. "Laurence Olivier's brooding Max de Winter is a performance that almost does not need to be commented upon."

9. "Fredric March and Martha Scott, under the superbly lucid and restrained direction of Irving Rapper, infuse with warm and sentient life the characters of William Spencer and his wife."

10. "You'll love Mr. Coburn's Benjamin Dingle if you have a heart in your breast."

a) *One Foot in Heaven*
b) *Our Town.*
c) *Mr. Smith Goes to Washington*
d) *What Price Glory*
e) *Wuthering Heights*
f) *Grand Hotel*
g) *Rebecca*
h) *Frankenstein*
i) *The More the Merrier*
j) *You Can't Take it With You*

124. BEVERLY HILLS FOLKS

1. Who was Miss New Orleans of 1931?

* * *

2. Who was Miss Burbank of 1948?

* * *

3. Who was Miss Hungary of 1936?

* * *

4. What kind of car was James Dean killed in?

* * *

5. Mia Farrow starred in *Rosemary's Baby.* Name a film about the devil that her father directed.

* * *

6. Who played Eve in *All About Eve?*

* * *

7. Who played King Arthur (*Lancelot and Guinevere*) and Emperor Maximilian (*Juarez*)?

* * *

8. Who was nominated for an Oscar as Best Supporting Actress in 1946 (*The Spiral Staircase*) and in 1949 (*Pinky*)?

* * *

9. Who played Col. Davenport in *Twelve O'Clock High?*

✳   ✳   ✳

10. In what movie did Gene Kelly dance with a mouse?

†   †   †

125.   SCHOOL DAZE

† † † † †

1.   Who is Archie Andrews' coach?

* * *

2.   What was Jack Armstrong's school?

* * *

3.   Where did Mr. Peepers teach?

* * *

4.   Where did Mr. Novak teach?

* * *

5.   Where did Miss Brooks teach?

* * *

6.   Where was the *Blackboard Jungle?*

* * *

7.   Where did Archie Andrews go to school?

† † †

126. BEAR IN MIND

† † † † †

1. New England telephone operators in 1923 earned an average of: a) $10 a week; b) $22 a week; or c) $50 a week.

* * *

2. In 1923 the wholesale price of beef was: a) 12c-17c a pound; b) 25c a pound; or c) 40c a pound.

* * *

3. In 1923, an Army private received: a) 67c a day; b) 75c a day; or c) $1.00 a day.

* * *

4. Edouard Daladier, Paul Reynaud, Maurice Gamelin and Maxime Weygand were: a) French scientists and inventors; b) French athletes; c) French statesmen and military men; or d) French dress designers.

* * *

5. The 1932 Stimson Doctrine: a) reaffirmed the Monroe Doctrine; b) proclaimed that the United States would not recognized territorial changes made in violation of international anti-war treaties; or c) removed all soldiers from the U.S.-Canada border.

* * *

6. The 1932 London Naval Conference: a) banned battleships and other war vessels from using the Panama Canal; b) displayed the latest armaments including the newly invented aircraft carrier; or c) gave signatories the right to increase the size of their navies under special circumstances.

* * *

7. The National Origins Act: a) allowed people to change their names; b) restricted immigration; or c) prohibited the sale of certain imports.

* * *

8. The Kellogg-Briand Pact: a) outlawed war; b) permitted limited combat and trench warfare; c) legalized the sale of cold cereals in chain stores; or d) registered trademarks and brand-names.

* * *

9. The Rust Brothers invented a) 3-in-1 Oil; b) the automatic cotton picker; c) anti-freeze; or d) hydraulic fluid controls.

* * *

10. The Watson-Parker Act of 1926: a) provided for a national arbitration board to settle railroad disputes; b) provided for parking lots in front of Federal courthouses; or c) supplied free pens and ink in post offices.

127. OLD TIMERS' DAY

† † † † †

1. Who holds the American League record for longevity as a player (25 years)?

* * *

2. Who was the first man to play two major pro sports (basketball and baseball) in the same city? What city?

* * *

3. Who was the first baseman (Brooklyn Dodgers, Chicago Cubs) who quit baseball to become an actor?

* * *

4. Who was the only club trainer to become a big league manager?

* * *

5. Who was the only man to play, coach and manage in both leagues and umpire in one?

* * *

6. Who was the first big league catcher to wear glasses?

* * *

7. Who was the first American League player to become league president?

* * *

8. Who was the pitcher who used to wake up fans by calling hogs?

* * *

9. Who was the major league pitcher who became a sports cartoonist?

*   *   *

10. Who was the catcher who hit three homers in one game (July 26, 1939) and made the American League All-Star Team seven times?

†   †   †

128.   CRITICAL GUESSES, #8

† † † † †

What film is the Times' *reviewer talking about?*

1. "Mary Beth Hughes has been pulled in for one brief, ironic scene with Mr. Fonda which gives a justification for his mood."
2. "Little Margaret O'Brien makes a wholly delightful imp of Satan, as Tootie, and Lucille Bremmer is lovely and old-fashioned as Rose, the nubile sis."
3. "Not only has the original stage play of Garson Kanin been preserved by screenwriter Albert Manheimer in all of its flavorsome detail—but George Cukor has directed with regard for both the humor and the moral."
4. "It is played with corruscating vigor by Linda Darnell in the golddigger role and by Paul Douglas, the rough-cut big shot."
5. "As the mercenary suitor, Montgomery Clift seems a little young and a wee bit too glibly modern in his verbal inflections and attitudes."
6. "Alfonso Bedoya is both colorful and revealing as an animalistic bandit chief."
7. "Olivia de Havilland does a brilliant, heart-rending job as the central guilt-ridden patient."
8. "Shaped by Moss Hart into a screen play of notable nimbleness and drive, the bewilderments of Miss Hobson's hero become absorbing."
9. "Elia Kazan has directed this picture, his first, with an easy naturalness that has brought out all the tone of real experience."
10. "Mr. Hitchock has used some startling images to symbolize the content of dreams—images designed by Salvador Dali."
11. "Anne Revere and Donald Crisp are splendid as the little girl's mother and dad."

a) *Meet Me In St. Louis*
b) *National Velvet*
c) *Spellbound*
d) *A Letter to Three Wives*
e) *A Tree Grows in Brooklyn*
f) *Gentleman's Agreement*
g) *The Snake Pit*
h) *The Ox-Bow Incident*
i) *The Treasure of the Sierra Madre*
j) *The Heiress*
k) *Born Yesterday*

129. FILM BITS

† † † † †

1. Susan Hayward was William Lundigan's bride in what movie?

* * *

2. Louise Dresser played Melissa Frake in what movie?

* * *

3. The small town barber in *What Till the Sun Shines, Nellie* was played by whom?

* * *

4. Nick Adams received his Oscar nomination as Best Supporting Actor for what film?

* * *

5. In what movie did Dorothy Lamour first appear in a sarong?

* * *

6. John Barrymore and Melvyn Douglas both played what identical role?

* * *

7. Name the actress who appeared in all of these: *Mother Carey's Chickens, Yes, My Darling Daughter* and *Daughters Courageous.*

* * *

8. Name the actress to appear in all these "number" movies: *Twenty Mule Team, Five Graves to Cairo, One Desire, The Ten Commandments, Three Violent People,* and *Summer of the Seventeenth Doll.*

* * *

168

9. Name the actor who appeared in all these "mad" movies: *The Mad Empress, The Mad Doctor of Market Street, Man-Made Monster, The Secret of Madame Blanche,* and *Last Train from Madrid.*

* * *

10. What do Walter Brennan, Edgar Buchanan and Paul Newman have in common?

† † †

130. REAL NAMES, #3

† † † † †

Match the pseudonym and the real name.

1.	Frankie Laine	a)	Lewis D. Offield
2.	Nora Bayes	b)	Stanley Morner
3.	Jack Oakie	c)	Frank Paul Lovecchio
4.	Jane Powell	d)	Dora Goldberg
5.	Ziggy Elman	e)	Suzanne Burce
6.	Dennis Morgan	f)	Eleanor Gough
7.	Alvino Rey	g)	Marjorie Chandler
8.	Billie Holiday	h)	Harry Finkelman
9.	Dorothy Collins	i)	Yvonne Marie Jamais
10.	Connie Haines	j)	Alvin McGurney

† † †

131. LOOKING BACK

1. The 1923 Adkins vs. Childrens Hospital Supreme Court decision: a) declared a minimum wage law unconstitutional; b) gave states the right to close down childrens hospitals; or c) required army bases to establish childrens hospitals for dependents.

* * *

2. The 1924 Bonus Bill: a) granted World War veterans $1,000 in service certificates; b) gave farmers certain subsidies; or c) required key industries to pay employees bonuses.

* * *

3. What did Albert Fall, Harry Sinclair and Edward L. Doheny have in common?

* * *

4. What medium of entertainment came to a halt in 1958?

* * *

5. Who was shot down over Russia, May 1, 1960?

* * *

6. What mode of transit did Arthur G. Sherman invent?

* * *

7. Identify these two New York city phone numbers: a) MU 8-9933, b) PE 6-5000.

* * *

8. Who manufactured "The 1933 Silver Arrow"—a car with a 12-cylinder, 175 hp engine, with a cruising speed of 80 mph?

*   *   *

9. Who is Barbie Doll's boyfriend?

*   *   *

10. Who was the original Mellins Food Baby?

† † †

132. MOVIE SHORTS

1. Name the inspector played by Peter Sellers and Alan Arkin.

* * *

2. Name the inspector who appeared on "Boston Blackie."

* * *

3. Name the inspector pursued by Kimble in "The Fugitive."

* * *

4. Name Simenon's detective.

* * *

5. Who was shot by Brigid O'Shaughnessy with a .38 Webley at Bush and Burritt Streets?

* * *

6. What's the missing Paul Newman "H" movie? *The Helen Morgan Story, The Hustler, Hud, Harper, Hall of Mirrors . . .*

* * *

7. Who wrote the music for *Kings Row, Anthony Adverse, The Private Lives of Elizabeth and Essex, The Sea Hawk, The Prince and the Pauper, The Constant Nymph* and *The Adventures of Robin Hood?*

* * *

8. Who composed the score for *To Kill a Mockingbird?*

* * *

9. Who wrote the music for the movies, *Henry V* and *Hamlet?*

* * *

10. What did Neal Dodd and Robert H. Dunn have in common?

† † †

133. REAL NAMES, #4

† † † † †

Match the pseudonym and the real name.

1. Sophie Tucker   a) Alfred Arnold Cocozza

2. Andy Russell   b) Donna Mae Tjaden

3. Ann Miller   c) George Tunnell

4. Mae Murray   d) Mary Elfrieda Winn

5. Janis Paige   e) Samuel Goldberg

6. Buddy Clark   f) Giovanni Alfredo DeSimons

7. Mary Lou Williams   g) Sonia Kalish

8. Bon Bon   h) Andy Rabajos

9. Mario Lanza   i) Marie Koenig

10. Johnny Desmond   j) Lucille Ann Collier

† † †

134. HOMERS AND MEMORIES

1. Who was the only American League outfielder to make 500 putouts in one year?

* * *

2. Who was the first black player in the American League?

* * *

3. How many double plays did the combination of Tinkers to Evers to Chance actually account for?

* * *

4. Who holds the American League record of pitching three no-hit games?

* * *

5. Who had the best lifetime record for pitchers in the majors?

* * *

6. Who hit the most homers as a pinch-hitter?

* * *

7. Who got nine hits in one game?

* * *

8. Who was called Babe Ruth's "caddy"?

* * *

9. Who was the Tiger catcher who was beaned in the head in May 1937 and never played again?

*   *   *

10. Who was the Yankee player—American League Rookie of the Year (1949)—who rejoined the service to fly 120 missions in Korea, and returned home to hit .364 in the 1957 World Series against the Braves?

†   †   †

135. TAKE UP A RECOLLECTION

† † † † †

1. What did Postmaster General Summerfield and Interior Secretary McKay in Ike's Cabinet have in common?

* * *

2. What was the "Nautilus"?

* * *

3. What Saturday evening comedy hour folded in 1954 after 160 weeks?

* * *

4. Define these hot-rod terms: a) skins; b) snowballs; c) chopping; d) raking; e) spooking.

* * *

5. What was the name of the San Francisco enterprise located at 261 Columbus Avenue? What was it named after?

* * *

6. Who was the famous zoologist who measured and preserved over three million gall wasps?

* * *

7. Who was Eisenhower's TV coach?

* * *

8. What drug did Dr. Louis Lasagna administer to Boston volunteers in 1952?

* * *

9. What was the "Look Ahead, Neighbor" Special?

*   *   *

10. What happened to most of the Japanese Second Army during World War II?

†   †   †

ACROSS

1. Aviator and polar explorer (4).
3. Dempsey's promoter (3, 7).
10. Hays Code no-nos (5).
11. Press agent's goal (9).
12. Lawrence Talbot was afflicted with one (5).
13. Gypsy Rose Lee (8).
15. Double-decker (7).
16. Kubelsky was Jack Benny's real one (7).
19. Singer Teresa ——— and her family (7).
21. *Divorce,* ——— *Style* (7).
22. Typhoid Mary caused one (8).
25. ——— Flow, British naval base in both World Wars (5).
27. Product of a barbershop quartet (9).
28. Bob Hope's tool in *The Paleface* (5).
29. He won the U.S. singles tennis title seven times in the 20s (4, 6).
30. ——— *White and the Seven Dwarfs* (4).

DOWN

1. Harry Lillis (4, 6).
2. The Galloping Ghost (3, 6).
4. *Confidential* Magazine's specialties (7).
5. Author of *Northwest Passage* (7).
6. Cheta (5).
7. Faye (5).
8. Doris and Laraine (4).
9. Put together (8).
14. Platinum blonde (4, 6).
17. Burma Shave signs used to clutter the ——— (8).
18. Revolutionary technique (9).
20. Phrase not heard these days: "What in the ———?" (3, 4).
21. Airwick's ancestor? (7).
23. Senator Ed Ford, Harry Hershfield and Joe Laurie, Jr., for instance (5).
24. To move aimlessly (5).
26. Middleweight champ, 1923-26 (4).

Quiz-Word No. 9

136. REAL NAMES, #5

† † † † †

Match the pseudonym and the real name.

1. Patti Page   a) Marietta Williams

2. Red Norvo   b) Vera Jane Palmer

3. Marilyn Miller   c) Francis T. Durgin

4. Vic Damone   d) Vito Farinola

5. Rhonda Fleming   e) Marilyn Louis

6. Rory Calhoun   f) Martha Reed

7. Jayne Mansfield   g) Gertrude Pridgett

8. Ma Rainey   h) Clara Ann Fowler

9. Martha Raye   i) Kenneth Norville

10. Maxine Sullivan   j) Mary Ellen Reynolds

† † †

137.   BALCONY SEATS

1.   Who played Caesar Enrico Bandello?

* * *

2.   What was the movie version of Harold Robbins' *A Stone for Danny Fisher?*

* * *

3.   Name the rival gangs in *West Side Story.*

* * *

4.   Who sang "How Little We Know" in Gerard's Cafe?

* * *

5.   Who narrated *Godzilla?*

* * *

6.   Francis the Mule starred with Donald O'Connor in 6 films. Name the one picture Francis appeared in with Mickey Rooney.

* * *

7.   Who played Captain Jacobi in *The Maltese Falcon?*

* * *

8.   Who played Captain Kinrose in *In Which We Serve?*

* * *

9. Trigger was Roy Rogers' horse. What was his dog's name?

* * *

10. What kind of auto did Bullitt drive?

† † †

138. REMINDERS

1. *Time* Magazine's Man of the Year in 1956 was Harlow Curtice. Who was he?

* * *

2. Whose father commented about his daughter's 1956 marriage: "She went on the French Riviera to make a picture called *To Catch a Thief*—and look what she came back with!"

* * *

3. In October, 1957, an NBC newsman told his listeners: "Listen now for the sound which forevermore separates the old from the new." To what was he referring?

* * *

4. What was opened to traffic on April 25, 1959?

* * *

5. What are the two most famous products of the Wham-O Mfg. Company?

* * *

6. Who had "fished along in a skiff in the Gulf Stream and had gone eighty-four days now without taking a fish?"

* * *

7. What would you "shout over a mike or a phone, or from the highest steeple"?

* * *

8. Who stated on 1952 TV that all he owned was a 1950 Olds, $3,000 equity in his California house, $20,000 equity in his Washington house, $4,000 in life insurance plus GI term insurance?

*   *   *

9. What did a pilot in 1947 sight flying over the Takima, Washington, Indian Reservation at 1,200 mph?

*   *   *

10. What do-it-yourself craze was invented by the Palmer Paint Company of Detroit?

† † †

139. AN ORIGINAL WORK

1. Who wrote *King of the Khyber Rifles?*
2. Who wrote *The Black Swan?*
3. Who wrote *The General Died at Dawn?*
4. Who wrote *Christopher Bean?*
5. Who wrote "The Pride of the Yankees"?
6. Who wrote *Way Down East?*
7. Who wrote *The Bravados?*
8. Who wrote *The Song of Bernadette?*
9. Who wrote "The Strange Love of Martha Ivers"?
10. Who wrote *Goodbye, Mr. Chips:*

a) James Hilton
b) Frank O'Rourke
c) John Patrick
d) Paul Gallico
e) Charles G. Booth
f) Talbot Mundy
g) Franz Werfel
h) Lottie Blair Parker
i) Sidney Howard
j) Rafael Sabatini

140. REAL NAMES, #6

† † † † †

Match the pseudonym and the real name.

1. Tony Martin   a) Alphonso D'Abruzzo

2. Kay Starr   b) Benjamin Anzelwitz

3. Joni James   c) Jeanne de la Fonte

4. Danny Kaye   d) Katherine Starks

5. Renee Adoree   e) Alvin Morris

6. Gilda Gray   f) David Kuminsky

7. Harriet Hilliard   g) Joan Carmello Babbo

8. Robert Alda   h) Marianne Michaelska

9. Ben Bernie   i) Peggy Lou Snyder

10. Wee Bonnie Baker   j) Evelyn Nelson

† † †

141. RADIO LINKS

† † † † †

1. Who was the Lone Ranger's nephew?
2. Who was Baby Snooks' "Daddy"?
3. Who was Corliss Archer's boyfriend?
4. Who was Henry Aldrich's sister?
5. Who was Bill Davidson's daughter?
6. Who was The Great Gildersleeve's maid?
7. Who was Amos Jones' daughter?
8. Who was Lorenzo Jones' wife?
9. Who was Stella Dallas' daughter?
10. Who was Vic and Sade's uncle?

a) Mary
b) Belle
c) Dan Reid
d) Hanley Stafford
e) Dexter Franklin
f) Fletcher
g) Laurel
h) Arbadella
i) Birdie Lee Coggins
j) Nancy Donovan

† † †

142. 30s POT POURRI

1. What was the name of General Motor's landscape of tomorrow at the 1939 New York World's Fair?

* * *

2. Who was Elizabeth Angela Marguerite Bowes-Lyon?

* * *

3. What was the first feature-length Technicolor movie?

* * *

4. Why did FDR invoke the Trading With the Enemy Act in 1933?

* * *

5. Who was the only car-maker not to endorse the NRA?

* * *

6. Who wrote *My First Days in the White House?*

* * *

7. How many press conferences did FDR hold: a) 249; b) 576; c) 751; or d) 998?

* * *

8. The Gross National Product for 1939 was: a) $88.6 billion; b) $150 billion; or c) 250 billion.

* * *

9. What did SLID stand for?

*   *   *

10. Who said, "He who tooteth not his own horn, the same shall not be tooted."?

†   †   †

143. BROTHERS AND SISTERS

1. Name Guy Lombardo's brothers and their instruments.

    *   *   *

2. What were the names of Mrs. Goldberg's children?

    *   *   *

3. Name both sets of Bobbsey Twins.

    *   *   *

4. Name the three Boswell sisters.

    *   *   *

5. Name the car made by Horace and John.

    *   *   *

6. Name the car made by Gaston and Louis.

    *   *   *

7. Name the car made by August and Frederick.

    *   *   *

8. Name the Everly Brothers.

    *   *   *

9. Name Ma Perkins' daughters.

    *   *   *

10. Name the Mayo Brothers.

*   *   *

11. Name the McGuire Sisters.

† † †

144. IN RETROSPECT

✝ ✝ ✝ ✝ ✝

1. What was the Army's World War II demobilization plan called?

* * *

2. Who were the Militant Marketers of 1946?

* * *

3. What were the "Wanna-Go-Home" riots?

* * *

4. What was the GOP slogan dreamed up by the Frost advertising agency in 1946?

* * *

5. Whom did the Americans for Democratic Action seek for the Democratic Presidential nomination in 1948?

* * *

6. What was the card game name suggested by the tray placed on the table to hold the cards?

* * *

7. Who wrote *Came a Cavalier?*

* * *

8. Who was the portrait painter present at President Roosevelt's death?

* * *

9. Who awarded General Eisenhower a medal set with 91 matched 16-carat diamonds?

*   *   *

10. What was the name of the document concerned with the surrender of Japan?

†   †   †

ACROSS

1. Uncle Dave Macon was great on this (3, 5).
5. "The Walter Winchell ———" (6).
9. Woolies were often like this (8).
10. Indian statesman (6).
12. Buddy Rich and Gene Krupa sat behind it (1, 4).
13. "Professor Quiz" and "Uncle Jim's Question Bee" were probably the first big ones (4, 5).
14. James Dunn won a Best Supporting Actor Oscar for ——— Brooklyn (1, 4, 5, 2).
19. He wrote How to Win Friends & Influence People (4, 8).
22. Doctrine (9).
25. "——— Sanctum" (5).
26. "The score stood four to two with but one ——— left to play" ("Casey at the Bat") (6).
27. Imaginers (8).
28. Once made of bamboo (6).
29. Tool of Jose Capablanca's trade (4, 3).

DOWN

1. Major Italian dialect (6).
2. Ruth's lifetime record had very few of these (6).
3. .45 Colt (9).
4. The public personified (4, 1).
6. Chiefs (5).
7. Karloff, in Bedlam, headed one (8).
8. "Three Little Fishies" was ——— of 1939 (1, 3, 4).
11. "Oh, I wish I was ——— again to do what I did again!" (6).
15. James Reese ———, pioneer popular orchestra leader (6).
16. Better than copies (9).
17. A favorite theme of child movies (8).
18. Hitler and Stalin made an unholy one (8).
20. ——— with Dirty Faces (6).
21. Rathskeller toast (6).
23. Tyrone Power built one in Suez (5).
24. The Day The ——— Stood Still (5).

Quiz-Word No. 10

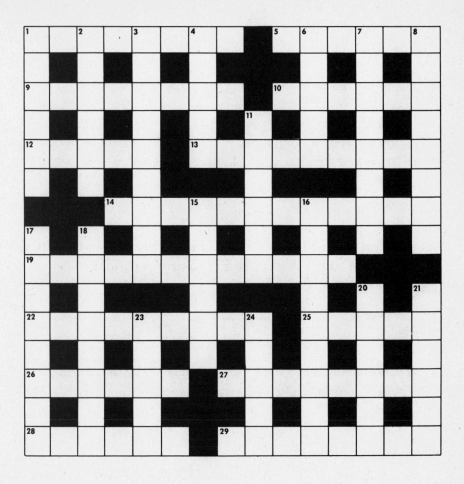

SEMI-OFFICIAL
NOSTALGIA DIARY

January 1
What movie opened this day, 1941? It starred Monty Woolley, Bette Davis and Ann Sheridan.

* * *

January 2
What movie opened this day, 1922? Directed by D. W. Griffith, it starred Lillian and Dorothy Gish as sisters separated during the French Revolution.

* * *

January 3
What fund-raising drive was begun this day, 1938? Basil O'Connor and Eddie Cantor had a lot to do with promoting it.

* * *

January 4
What radio series premiered this day, 1931? It was a story of back-stage life and its theme was "Poor Butterfly."

* * *

January 5
What invention was demonstrated this day, 1940? It was developed by Major E. H. Armstrong.

* * *

January 6
What movie actress was born this day, 1913? She won an Oscar for her role as a Swedish girl who runs for Congress.

* * *

January 7
Who was the financier appointed U.S. Ambassador to Great Britain this day, 1938? He had been commissioner of the S.E.C., and also had a brief career as a Hollywood mogul.

* * *

January 8
Who became President of France this day, 1959?

* * *

January 9
What entertainer was born this day, 1914? Her movies include *Belle of the Yukon* and *Wind Across the Everglades,* but she's remembered for her contributions to another form of entertainment. Her real name: Louise Hovick.

* * *

January 10
In 1952, this day, Captain Henrik K. Carlsen made headlines by refusing to leave his sinking ship. What was its name?

* * *

January 11
What movie was the first to be shown at the Radio City Music Hall, New York City, on this day, 1933?

* * *

January 12

How did Mrs. Hattie Caraway of Arkansas make history this day, 1933?

* * *

January 13

What geographic region voted this day, 1935, to return to Germany?

* * *

January 14

Who met this day, 1943, in Casablanca?

* * *

January 15

Who was the eminent concert pianist who, this day, 1919, became the first premier of a new nation? What was his nation?

* * *

January 16

Who was the movie actress who was killed this day, 1942? Her real name was Jane Peters.

* * *

January 17

In what city was an armored car bearing $1.5 million stolen this day, 1950?

* * *

January 18

Who was the English writer who died this day, 1936? Quote from his work: "For the Colonel's Lady an' Judy O'Grady are sisters under their skins!"

* * *

January 19

Who was the aviator who set a transcontinental air record this day, 1937, by flying across the U.S. in 7 hours, 28 minutes?

*   *   *

January 20

What movie opened this day, 1929? It was the first full-length talkie shot on location. Warner Baxter played The Cisco Kid; Raoul Walsh directed it.

*   *   *

January 21

What was the name of the first atomic submarine launched, this day, 1954?

*   *   *

January 22

The first commercial television station west of the Mississippi opened this day, 1947. Was it located in a) Denver; b) Seattle; or c) Hollywood?

*   *   *

January 23

This actor was born this day, 1899. In 1942, a film starring him as a nightclub owner opened this day. And in 1948 a film starring him as a gold prospector opened this day. Name the actor and the two movies.

*   *   *

January 24

In 1935 this day barrels, pumps, bottles and an old custom called "rushing the growler" suddenly became old hat. Why?

*   *   *

January 25

Who was the notorious Indiana gangster captured this day in Tucson, Ariz?

* * *

January 26

What was the name of the famed hotel in Cairo burned this day, 1952?

* * *

January 27

The first all-American air raid was staged this day in 1944. What was the target: a) Dresden; b) Wilhelmshaven; or c) Berlin?

* * *

January 28

In 1934 this day, in Woodstock, Vt., what important skiing invention was introduced?

* * *

January 29

Called "The Hunk," this movie actor was born this day, 1916. He played Doc Holliday in *My Darling Clementine* and Samson in *Samson and Delilah*. Name him.

* * *

January 30

Born this day, 1882, he later became an assistant Secretary of the Navy. He married a distant cousin. And his dog's name was Fala. Name him.

* * *

January 31
Born this day, 1875, he went to dental school on a baseball scholarship. Though one of America's most successful writers, he was proudest of his deep-sea fishing exploits. Several of his records still stand. Name him.

* * *

February 1
Also known as Sean O'Fearna, this director was born this day, 1895. He directed over 125 features, including *Arrowsmith, The Lost Patrol, The Informer* and *Stagecoach.* Name him.

* * *

February 2
This Irish writer was born this day, 1882. Almost blind, he managed to write several books which turned literature topsy-turvy. Joseph Strick directed a 1967 movie based on one of his books, the story of a Dublin Jew. Name him.

February 3
This day, 1943, George Fox, Alexander Goode, Clark Poling and John Washington went down with their ship. Who were these men?

* * *

February 4
This day, 1932, the Winter Olympics opened in what American resort town?

* * *

February 5
This day, 1937, Pres. Roosevelt announced that he planned to change the Surpeme Court. What was his plan?

* * *

February 6
Released this day, 1931, it was a silent movie when all others were talkies. Nevertheless its magic caught the imagination of film-goers. It starred Charles Chaplin in his last silent role. The picture's name?

* * *

February 7
Today, 1937, a radio show originally called "Sidewalk Interviews" began on CBS. Its new name was a Latin tag. It featured Warren Hull as M.C. What was the name of this long-running quiz and interview program?

* * *

February 8
This day, 1910, a group, based on Kipling's *Jungle Book*, military lessons learned during The Boer War, and the experience of an American newspaperman in London was organized. Daniel Beard was for a long time associated with the group. Its name?

* * *

February 9
What was the French liner that burned and capsized this day, 1942, in New York?

* * *

February 10
What form of cheap entertainment debuted this day, 1933? It was written by an amateur and presented by a boy at your door.

* * *

February 11
Fated to be the last king of his country, he was born this day, 1920. Because he showed pro-Axis sympathies, the British imposed a premier sympathetic to the Allies on his country. In 1958 he

was deprived of his citizenship and moved to Monaco. Who was he?

* * *

February 12
What movie opened this day, 1932? It starred Marlene Dietrich, Anna May Wong, Clive Brooks and Warner Oland.

* * *

February 13
Born this day, 1933, this film actress was touted by Columbia as Monroe's rival. She was in *Picnic, Pal Joey* and *Pushover.* Name her.

* * *

February 14
What movie opened this day, 1931? Karl Freund was the photographer and Tod Browning directed it. The movie had been intended to be a vehicle for Lon Chaney, who died, forcing Browning to choose an actor who had appeared in his 1929 film, *The Thirteenth Chair.* Universal's advertising slogan completely misrepresented the movie: "The Strangest Love A Man Has Ever Known."

* * *

February 15
Who was assassinated this day, 1933, by an out-of-work bricklayer?

* * *

February 16
Who was the movie actor born this day, 1901? He played Boston Blackie in some 12 films.

* * *

February 17

Who was the European king killed this day, 1934, while mountain climbing?

* * *

February 18

What discovery was made this day, 1930, by Clyde W. Tombaugh? The discovery had been predicted 11 years earlier by W. H. Pickering.

* * *

February 19

What movie opened this day, 1936? It starred Sylvia Sidney and Henry Fonda and was directed by Henry Hathaway.

* * *

February 20

Why was the gloomy prediction that "we're going to the dogs" vindicated this day, 1920, in Emeryville, California?

* * *

February 21

One million men were killed in this battle, which began today, 1916. What battle was it?

* * *

February 22

What actor was born this day, 1907? He made his movie debut in *The Sin of Madelon Claudet,* appeared in *Claudia* and *The Enchanted Cottage,* and starred on TV as first an insurance agent and then a doctor.

* * *

February 23

On this day in 1945 U.S. Marines raised the Stars and Stripes over what high point in the Pacific?

* * *

February 24

What Filipino city was liberated today, 1945?

* * *

February 25

Which great player left the Yankees this day, 1935?

* * *

February 26

The Poor Soul was born this day, 1916. He's also known as "Minnesota Fats." Who is he?

* * *

February 27

Who was the movie actress born this day, 1932? As a child she was evacuated from England to Hollywood. Her movies include *The Rich, Full Life, Conspirator* and *Beau Brummell.*

* * *

February 28

Who was the cartoonist born this day, 1907? His comic strips include *Terry and the Pirates, Steve Canyon* and *Male Call.*

* * *

February 29

Henry Stimson took office this day, 1928, as a) Secretary of War; b) Governor General of the Phillipines; or c) Commissioner of Organized Baseball?

* * *

March 1
Who was the twenty-month-old baby kidnapped this day, 1932?

*   *   *

March 2
What movie was released this day, 1933? It starred Fay Wray and the largest co-star ever seen.

*   *   *

March 3
Who was the movie star born this day, 1911? Her real name was Harlean Carpentier, and she debuted in the Laurel & Hardy short, *Double Whoopee.*

*   *   *

March 4
Whose inauguration was broadcast this day, 1929?

*   *   *

March 5
Who was the movie star born this day, 1908? His original name was Reginald Carey, and he debuted in *The Great Game.* He's played the King of Siam, a medieval pope and Saladin.

*   *   *

March 6
Who was the pitcher born this day, 1900? He chalked up 300 American League wins; pitched in 616 games; his winning percentage was .682.

*   *   *

March 7
Into what part of Europe did Germany march into this day, 1936?

*   *   *

March 8
Who was the movie star born this day, 1912? Her real last name was Wemlinger. She won an Oscar in 1948 for her supporting work in *Key Largo*.

* * *

March 9
Who invaded Columbus, New Mexico, this day, 1916?

* * *

March 10
Who was the Irish movie star born this day, 1888? His real name was William Shields and he made his movie debut in *Juno and the Paycock*.

* * *

March 11
Who was the former President and Supreme Court Chief Justice buried this day, 1930, in Arlington National Cemetary?

* * *

March 12
FDR gave his first informal broadcast this day, 1933. What were these radio programs called?

* * *

March 13
This day, 1928, the St. Francis dam burst. Over 450 people were killed. Where did this happen?

* * *

March 14.
What movie opened this day, 1946? It starred Rita Hayworth and a song called "Put the Blame on Mame."

March 15

Ah, yes, what was the W.C. Fields movie that opened this day, 1940? Writing credits went to Cuthbert J. Twillie and Flower Belle Lee.

*   *   *

March 16

What did Robert Goddard accomplish this day, 1926?

*   *   *

March 17

This day, 1953, which of the following happened: a) World War II price controls finally came to an end; b) the automatic coffeemaker was invented; or c) Bardahl was invented?

*   *   *

March 18

A former Pacific kingdom made headlines this day, 1959. How?

*   *   *

March 19

Who received the Woodrow Wilson medal and $25,000 this day, 1928; a) Charles A. Lindbergh; b) Frank Kellogg; or c) Herbert Hoover?

*   *   *

March 20

Called the greatest of all heldentenors, this Great Dane was born this day, 1890, Who was he?

*   *   *

March 21

A marriage in Kentucky this day, 1891, ended what notorious feud?

March 22

In 1941 this day, which dam began to produce electrical power?

* * *

March 23

Who was the aviatrix who flew this day, 1935, from Pearl Harbor to San Francisco?

* * *

March 24

Today, 1932, the first broadcast was made: a) from a moving train; b) an airplane; or c) the Eiffel Tower?

* * *

March 25

RCA today, 1954, began: a) first commercial production of color TV; b) production of the Extended Play record; or c) experimenting with stereophonic sound?

* * *

March 26

In 1937, this day, a statue to a fictional character was dedicated. He had made his debut on February 17, 1929, in a comic strip, *Thimble Theatre,* drawn by Elzie Segar. His "Sweet Patootie" was Olive and his "adoptik infink" was "Swee'pea." Name him.

* * *

March 27

What was the important announcement that General Dwight D. Eisenhower made today, 1945?

* * *

March 28

Who was the military hero who died this day, 1969?

* * *

211

March 29

Who was the singer born this day, 1918? She's appeared in *Carmen Jones, Porgy and Bess, That Certain Feeling.* Her hit songs include "Tired" and "Takes Two to Tango."

* * *

March 30

What was the radio show that began this day, 1935? It was moderated by George V. Denny, Jr., and orginated from New York City's Town Hall.

* * *

March 31

Two radio personalities were born this day. "The Old Redhead" was born in 1903, and a broadcaster whose theme song was "For He's a Jolly Good Fellow" was born in 1915. Name the two men.

* * *

April 1

This day in 1942, a singer made his last appearance with a band he had joined in 1940. He had appeared with this band in *Las Vegas Nights* and *Ship Ahoy,* and had recorded such songs as "I'll Be Seeing You", "Fools Rush In," and "I'll Never Smile Again" with them. Name the singer and the band.

* * *

April 2

In 1914, on this day, an English actor was born. Among the movie roles he played are Fagin, Disraeli, Herbert Pockett, Charles I and Hitler, and he won an Oscar for his work in *The Bridge on the River Kwai.* Name him.

* * *

April 3

Can you name the dance band singer and movie star who was born this day, 1924? She had begun as a dancer, later turned to singing, and had a hit with "Sentimental Journey" in 1944.

* * *

April 4
What was the name of the Navy aircraft that fell into the Atlantic this day, 1933?

* * *

April 5
Born this day, 1901, this movie actor won a Best Supporting Oscar in *Hud.* Can you name him.

* * *

April 6
In 1955, on this day, a British statesman, later known as Lord Avon, became Prime Minister. What was his name?

* * *

April 7
Who was the American industrialist who died this day, 1947, at the age of 83? Before going into business for himself he had been the chief engineer of the Edison Illuminating Company in Detroit. By 1933, he was employing 100,000 people. His profit-sharing plan, begun in 1914, distributed more than 10 million dollars a year to his workers.

* * *

April 8
What was the law that the Supreme Court declared unconstitutional this day, 1895: a) municipal speeding regulations; b) the income tax; or c) the right of workers to join unions?

* * *

213

April 9

Who was the singer born this day, 1898? He was an All-American end at Rutgers, and left the legal profession to star in such productions as *Emperor Jones, Othello* and *Show Boat*. His hit records include "Ol' Man River" and "Ballad for Americans."

*　*　*

April 10

What was the radio program that began broadcasting this day, 1936? The star's real name was Lester Kroll and he offered advice on personal problems.

*　*　*

April 11

Who was the baseball player who started work this day, 1947, with the Brooklyn Dodgers. In his best year, 1949, he had a .342 average, and was the National League's MVP 1949.

*　*　*

April 12

What movie was released this day, 1932? Vicki Baum had written the original book and Edmund Goulding directed it. It starred both Barrymore brothers, Garbo, Crawford and Beery.

April 13

The memorial dedicated this day, 1943, honored: a) Thomas Jefferson; b) Abraham Lincoln; or c) George Washington?

*　*　*

April 14

In what American city did an explosion this day, 1947, occur, killing 500 people?

*　*　*

April 15
Archie Leach's first film, *This Is the Night,* was released this day, 1932. What is Leach's film name?

*   *   *

April 16
Johnson Wax sponsored this radio show, which began this day, 1935. Some of the minor characters were Beulah, the maid, played by Marlin Hurt; The Old Timer, played by Cliff Arquette; Mayor La Trivia, played by Gale Gordon and Throckmorton P. Gildersleeve, played by Hal Peary. The show lasted until 1952. What was its name?

*   *   *

April 17
What was the site of the World's Fair that opened this day, 1958?

*   *   *

April 18
Today, 1934, saw the introduction in Ft. Worth, Texas, of: a) the laundromat; b) drip-grind coffee; or c) the neon sign?

*   *   *

April 19
Until January 1, 1975, the law made effective this day, 1933, was part of our monetary policy. What did this law do?

*   *   *

April 20
On this day, 1935, this radio show debuted over NBC. Over the years, its cast included Buddy Clark, Frank Sinatra, Bea Wain, Joan Edwards, Freda Biggson (Georgia Gibbs), Eileen Wilson, Doris Day, Lanny Ross, Dinah Shore, and Andy Russell. W. C. Fields often appeared. What was the name of this show?

*   *   *

April 21

Born in Mexico this day, 1915, this actor has been in movies since he was 21, making his first movie, *Parole,* in 1936. His Oscars were for his work in *Viva Zapata* and *Lust for Life.* Who is he?

* * *

April 22

What invention of Juan da la Cierva's landed this day, 1931, on the White House lawn?

* * *

April 23

Who was born this day, 1928? Today a stateswoman, her first career was as a movie actress, debuting in features in 1932 in *The Red-Haired Alibi.*

* * *

April 24

"A Terrible beauty is born." These lines by William Butler Yeats refer to what occasion of this day, 1916?

* * *

April 25

What opened this day, 1959: a) The Suez Canal; b) St. Lawrence Seaway; c) Alcan Highway; or d) The Lincoln Highway?

* * *

April 26

Who was elected this day, 1925, president of Germany: a) Adolf Hitler; b) Paul von Hindenburg; c) Wilhelm v. Hohenzollern; or d) Hermann Goering?

* * *

April 27

Who was the great baseball player born this day, 1896? He was the National League's batting champion seven times; his lifetime major league batting average was .358; and he may very well have been the best righthanded batter ever.

* * *

April 28

Who was the ex-political strongman who was captured and executed this day, 1945?

* * *

April 29

Today, 1913, Gideon Sunback of Hoboken, N.J. patented: a) the shoe-lace; b) the zipper; c) the electric typewriter; or d) the T-shirt?

* * *

April 30

Name the movie actress born this day, 1912. Her real name is Eunice Quedens. She originally was a Ziegfeld girl. Her successful radio show debuted in 1948 over CBS, and featured Jeff Chandler as a bashful colleague.

* * *

May 1

Today, 1909, "The Songbird of the South" was born. Her radio show debuted in 1936, and was known by her name and also as "The A&P Bandwagon." The show always began with these words: "It's high noon in New York." Who is she?

* * *

May 2

Born this day either 1901 or 1904 (the records are hazy), in Tacoma, Washington, this Gonzaga University alumnus was once part of a singing trio. He won an Oscar for his work in a 1944 picture. In 1936 he became the host of the "Kraft Music Hall." Name him.

* * *

May 3
This Oscar-winning actress was born 1906, as Lucille Langehanke. Her first talkie was *Ladies Love Brutes;* her last *Hush, Hush Sweet Charlotte.* In *Little Women* she played Marmee. Name her.

* * *

May 4
Name the Oscar-winning actress born this day, 1929. She has appeared in *One Wild Oat, Young Wives' Tale, Laughter in Paradise, Monte Carlo Baby* and *The Secret People.*

* * *

May 5
Name the movie actress born this day, 1915. She was discovered by Rudy Vallee, and debuted on his radio show as a singer, May, 1933. She was first married to Tony Martin. With her second husband she co-starred in a radio show, "The Fitch Bandwagon."

* * *

May 6
What movie starring Janet Gaynor and Charles Farrell opened this day, 1927? Frank Borzage directed it.

* * *

May 7
Name the movie actress born this day, 1923. She debuted in *Twenty-Mule Team.* Her greatest roles were probably in *The Razor's Edge* (Oscar here) and *All About Eve.*

* * *

May 8
Name the American statesman born this day, in Lamar, Mo., 1884. He served as an Artillery Captain during WWI. He retired in 1953, and published his memoirs in 1955-56.

*   *   *

May 9
Name the great tennis star born this day, 1928. He was Amateur Singles Champion, 1948-49.

*   *   *

May 10
On this day, 1940, the film biography of "The Sage of Menlo Park" opened with Spencer Tracy in the title role. Name the movie.

*   *   *

May 11
This surrealist artist was born this day, 1904. His most famous painting, "The Persistence of Memory," shows melted watches in an eerie landscape. Name him.

*   *   *

May 12
This great ball player was born this day, 1925. His records include: most Series played (14); most times as player on the winning team (10). He is known as a catcher, coach and manager. Name him.

*   *   *

May 13
This day, 1928, saw the opening of *Hangman's House*. Directed by John Ford, it "featured," in the role of a poor boy sentenced by a judge to hang, a USC football player who went on to appear in over 145 flicks, including "The Three Mesquiteers" series. Name him.

*   *   *

219

May 14

Today, 1929, saw first day of: a) airmail service between North and South America; b) The Morris Plan; or c) police car radios?

* * *

May 15

What movie opened today, 1931? Its theme song is "I'm Forever Blowing Bubbles," and in it Cagney pushes a grapefruit in Mae Clarke's face.

* * *

May 16

Who was the movie actress born this day, 1911? She starred in *Three Comrades, Shopworn Angel, The Shop Around the Corner* and *The Mortal Storm.*

* * *

May 17

What important sports event occured this day, 1939; a) the first college baseball game televised; b) first night game; or c) first after-game commentary broadcast?

* * *

May 18

What important bill was enacted this day, 1933? It established an agency authorized to produce fertilizer, among other things.

* * *

May 19

A ventriloquist, strong man and midget banded together in this movie, released this day, 1930. It was a sound remake of a 1925 classic, directed by Tod Browning.

* * *

May 20

Name the movie actor born this day, 1908. He won an Oscar for his job in *The Philadelphia Story.*

* * *

May 21

Name the Hollywood couple married this day, 1945. Their first movie together was *To Have and Have Not.*

* * *

May 22

This English actor was born this day, 1907. He has played Lord Nelson, Hamlet, Macheath and Richard III.

* * *

May 23

On this day, 1937, one of the richest men in the world died at 98. Name him.

* * *

May 24

On this day, 1935, Cincinatti saw a baseball first. What was it?

* * *

May 25

Who was the boxing champion born this day, 1897? He retired as heavyweight champ after defeating Tom Heeney on July 26, 1928.

* * *

May 26

Who was the folksinger who died this day, 1933? He was known as "The Singing Brakeman."

* * *

May 27

Name the movie actor born this day, 1911. He has appeared in *House of Wax, The House on Haunted Hill, The Fall of the House of Usher* and *House of a Thousand Dolls.*

* * *

May 28

Name the all-round athlete born this day, 1888. His exploits in the 1912 Olympics made him famous overnight. He played ball with the New York Giants, Cincinnati Reds, and Boston Braves.

* * *

May 29

What was the name given the veterans' demonstration in Washington that began this day, 1932?

* * *

May 30

Where did the riots occur this day, 1937, which resulted in 10 dead?

* * *

May 31

Over 800 blocks were ruined in this waterfront fire that occured this day, 1941. Where was the fire?

* * *

June 1

The first telecast prize fight was today, 1939. Who were the opponents: a) Braddock and Louis; b) Ross and Canzoneri; or c) Nova and Baer?

* * *

June 2

What is the name of the monarch crowned this day, 1953?

June 3
Who became the first player to hit four consecutive homers in one game? It happened this day, 1932.

* * *

June 4
What movie opened this day, 1942? It was directed by William Wyler, and concerned itself with an English family living under the German Blitz.

* * *

June 5
What was the name of the plan outlined this day, 1947, by the Secretary of State?

* * *

June 6
Where were all the cars going this day, 1933, in Camden, N.J.?

* * *

June 7
Who became the president of Columbia University this day, 1948?

* * *

June 8
Who offered to act as mediator between the Russians and Japanese this day, 1905?

* * *

June 9
Who is the movie actor born this day, 1910? (some records say 1908)? He starred in *It Started with Eve, King's Row, Saboteur,* and *Dial M for Murder.*

* * *

June 10

What was the name of the Czechoslovak village wiped out by the Nazis on this day, 1942?

* * *

June 11

What is the name of the scientist-film maker born this day, 1910? He is credited with the invention of the scuba lung.

* * *

June 12

Who is the singer born this day, 1928? His real name is Vito Farinola. He had a radio show on CBS, "Saturday Night Serenade," and appeared in *Rich, Young and Pretty, Deep in My Heart,* and *Kismet.*

* * *

June 13

In 1892 on this day, this British actor was born. Among the movies he appeared in were *David Copperfield, Anna Karenina, Captain Blood, Love From a Stranger, The Adventures of Robin Hood,* and a good many with Nigel Bruce as co-star. Who was he?

* * *

June 14

On this day, 1922, Warren Harding became the first president to do what?

* * *

June 15

Who is the jazz pianist born this day, 1923? He's the composer of "Misty."

* * *

June 16

Who was the opera soprano born this day, 1904? Her movie credits include *Deep in My Heart, The Ladies' Man* and *Gunn.*

* * *

June 17

Pan American Airways began what service today, 1947?

* * *

June 18

Who was the movie singer born this day, 1901? Her first movie was *The Love Parade,* her last *The Sun Comes Up.*

* * *

June 19

Name the band leader born this day, 1902. The slogan of his band: "The Sweetest Music This Side of Heaven."

* * *

June 20

Who is the playwright born this day, 1905? She wrote *The Litle Foxes, Watch on the Rhine* and *The Children's Hour.*

* * *

June 21

What was the name of the Libyan city that fell to the Germans today, 1942?

* * *

June 22

What country was attacked by the Germans today, 1941?

* * *

June 23

Who was the eminent Englishman born this day, 1894? At three times in his life he changed names. Give all three.

* * *

June 24

What was the movie that opened this day, 1943? Directed by Frank Borzage, it featured cameo appearances by Tallulah Bankhead, Katharine Hepburn, Harpo Marx, George Raft and others.

* * *

June 25

What movie opened this day, 1937? Taken from a Rudyard Kipling novel, it starred Spencer Tracy, who won an Oscar; Melvyn Douglas, Freddie Bartholomew and Lionel Barrymore.

* * *

June 26

Who was the best-selling novelist born this day, 1892? Her books include *Dragon Seed* and *The Good Earth*.

* * *

June 27

Who was the writer and lecturer born this day, 1880? Two movies were based on her life: *Deliverance* (1919) and *The Miracle Worker*.

* * *

June 28

Name the composer born this day, 1902. His songs include: "Thou Swell," "Ten Cents a Dance," "There's a Small Hotel," "The Blue Room," "I Didn't Know What Time It Was" . . . etc.

* * *

June 29

Whom did the Democrats nominate this day, 1928, for the presidency?

* * *

June 30

What book was published this day, 1936, by the Macmillan Company? It concerned itself with incidents that occured 70 years earlier around a property called "Tara."

* * *

July 1

Name the film that opened today, 1948. It featured Fred Astaire as a dancer with a new partner, Judy Garland.

July 2

Name the movie that opened today, 1941, with Gary Cooper in the title role. Joan Leslie played Gracie Williams and Walter Brennan played Pastor Rosier Pile.

* * *

July 3

Who was the movie actor born this day, 1906, in St. Petersburg, Russia. He won a Best Supporting Actor Oscar for *All About Eve*.

* * *

July 4

Name the Italian actress born this day, 1927. Her movies include *Beat the Devil, Trapeze* and *Solomon and Sheba*.

* * *

227

July 5

What New Deal agency was created this day, 1935, by passage of the Wagner-Connery Act?

*   *   *

July 6

In what city did the circus fire take place this day, 1944, which killed 168?

*   *   *

July 7

Which two Asiatic countries went to war this day, 1937?

*   *   *

July 8

Who was the movie actress who died this day, 1967? She starred in the movie made from the book published June 30, 1936, winning an Oscar for her role. She won another Oscar for her job in *A Streetcar Named Desire*.

*   *   *

July 9

Name the historian born this day, 1887. He won a Pulitzer Prize for his book *John Paul Jones*.

*   *   *

July 10

What happened to the dollar bill this day, 1929?

*   *   *

July 11

What new college was dedicated this day, 1955?

*   *   *

July 12

Prince Karim, a Harvard student, assumed a new role this day, 1957. What position did he take over?

* * *

July 13

Who was the vaudeville juggler who substituted for Will Rogers in the *Ziegfeld Follies* this night, 1925?

* * *

July 14

Who completed his round-the-world flight this day, 1938, in three days, nineteen hours, eight minutes?

* * *

July 15

To what country did President Eisenhower send the Marines this day, 1958?

* * *

July 16

What invention got its initiation today, 1935: a) the automatic parking meter; b) the electric can opener; or c) the extension phone?

* * *

July 17

What amusement park opened this day, 1955?

* * *

July 18

Who arrived in Ireland this day, 1938, "by accident?"

* * *

July 19

What Italian city was bombed for the first time this day, 1943?

*   *   *

July 20

Who escaped being blown up by a bomb planted at his headquarters this day, 1944?

*   *   *

July 21

Who was the writer born this day, 1899? In 1954 he won the Nobel Prize in literature. During the Spanish Civil War he reported it for American newspapers.

*   *   *

July 22

Who was the desperado killed this day, 1934, in front of a Chicago movie house?

*   *   *

July 23

Who was the detective story writer born this day, 1888? He was responsible for *Double Indemnity, Murder My Sweet, The Big Sleep, The Blue Dahlia, The Brasher Doubloon* and *Strangers on a Train.*

*   *   *

July 24

Who debated in a kitchen this day, 1959?

*   *   *

July 25

What two ocean liners collided this day, 1956?

*   *   *

230

July 26

Who is the Latin American revolutionary who began his revolt this day, 1953?

* * *

July 27

Name the baseball personality born this day, 1905, in W. Springfield, Mass. He justified his abrasiveness by saying, "Nice guys finish last."

* * *

July 28

Into what building did an Army plane crash this day, 1945, killing 13?

* * *

July 29

Against which country did Germany start its airblitz this day, 1940?

* * *

July 30

The WAVES were established this day, 1942. What does WAVE stand for?

* * *

July 31

On this day, 1948, President Truman dedicated the Idlewild airport. What name does this airport bear today?

* * *

August 1

Which coin went into circulation this day, 1932: a) The Silver Dollar; b) The Washington-Head Quarter; or c) The Lincoln Penny?

* * *

August 2
Name the movie actress born this day, 1905. She was often featured with William Powell in detective films.

* * *

August 3
What movie opened this day, 1929? It featured several brothers: Leonard, Adolph, Julius and Herbert.

* * *

August 4
Who was the Scots entertainer born this day, 1870? He was knighted for his fund-raising services during World War I, and he made several "farewell" tours of the U.S.

* * *

August 5
Today, 1926, the first talkie was released. Its name?

* * *

August 6
What film opened this day, 1937? It featured a lot of Occidentals disguised as Orientals. Luise Rainer won an Oscar for her work in the film.

* * *

August 7
Who was the Russian master spy indicted for espionage this day, 1957?

* * *

August 8
Name the movie actress born this day, 1910. Her real name is Sophia Kosow.

August 9

Who was the Indian nationalist interned by the British this day, 1942?

*   *   *

August 10

Name the redhaired movie actress born this day, 1923. Her real name is Marilyn Louis.

*   *   *

August 11

Who accepted the Republican nomination for President this day, 1928?

*   *   *

August 12

What film opened this day, 1927? It was the first movie to win an Oscar.

*   *   *

August 13

What important event happened this day, 1928, in Coytesville, N.J.?

*   *   *

August 14

Who won the first Olympic basketball game played this day, 1936?

August 15

Who were the two men killed in an airplane crash in Alaska this day, 1935?

*   *   *

233

August 16
Who was the movie actor who died this day, 1956? His films include *The Thirteenth Chair, The Black Camel, The Death Kiss,* and *The Invisible Ray.*

* * *

August 17
What political party held its convention this day, 1932, in St. Louis, Mo.?

* * *

August 18
Who was the American poet born this day, 1902? With Kurt Weill and S. J. Perelman he wrote "One Touch of Venus."

* * *

August 19
Who was the pioneer aviator who finally received a license by the CAA this day, 1946—43 years after his plane covered 852 feet in 59 seconds.

* * *

August 20
What was the name of the pioneer all-black musical to debut this day, 1929?

* * *

August 21
Who was the Russian revolutionary who died of wounds this day, 1940, in Mexico?

* * *

August 22
Name the two men nominated for second terms by the Republican party this day, 1956?

* * *

August 23
Who was the movie actor who died at the age of 31 this day, 1926, causing several women to kill themselves?

* * *

August 24
Name the mobster who surrendered to J. Edgar Hoover this day, 1939.

* * *

August 25
Name the film, D. W. Griffith's first talkie, which opened this day, 1930.

* * *

August 26
Today, 1920, the 19th Amendment went into effect. What did this Amendment do?

* * *

August 27
This day, 1940, what video innovation was publicly shown?

* * *

August 28
Name the French actor and the Swedish actress born this day. They appeared together in *Arch of Triumph* and *Gaslight*.

* * *

August 29
Name the jazz giant born this day, 1920. His alto sax technique lay the groundwork for progressive jazz.

* * *

235

August 30

Name the Canadian actor born this day, 1896. Among other parts, he's played Sherlock Holmes, John Brown, and Abraham Lincoln.

* * *

August 31

Who is the baseball star born this day, 1918? He was AL batting champ in 1941, 1942, 1947, 1948, 1957 and 1958.

* * *

September 1

Name the writer born this day, 1875. He created Tarzan of the Apes and John Carter of Mars.

* * *

September 2

What movie opened this day, 1937? It was the second version of the story. The first, 10 years earlier, starred Lewis Stone and Ramon Novarro. The second starred Ronald Colman and Douglas Fairbanks, Jr.

* * *

September 3

Name the musical comedy star born this day, 1915. Her real name is Catherine Holzman. She was married to Moss Hart. Her films include *Murder at the Vanities, She Loves Me Not, Here is My Heart* and *A Night at the Opera.*

* * *

September 4

On this day, 1927, this film opened. It was written by Ben Hecht and directed by Josef von Sternberg. It starred George Bancroft as Bull Weed, Evelyn Brent as Feathers McCoy and Clive Brook as Rolls Royce. Name the picture.

September 5
Who was the movie mogul born this day, 1902? For 17 years he was in charge of production for 20th Century-Fox, producing such movies as *Drums Along the Mohawk, The Grapes of Wrath, How Green Was My Valley, Gentlemen's Agreement,* and *Viva Zapata.*

* * *

September 6
On this day, 1925, *Pretty Ladies* opened. It is famous for the first screen appearance of an actress who was born Lucille le Sueur, changed her name to Billie Cassin, and changed it again. What is her name?

* * *

September 7
On this day, 1953, Lana Turner married her fourth husband. He played Tarzan in five pictures. Name him.

* * *

September 8
What was the name of the ship that burned this day, 1934?

* * *

September 9
On this day, 1943, Sonny Tufts made his first major movie. Stars included Claudette Colbert, Paulette Goddard, Veronica Lake, George Reeves and Barbara Britton. Name the movie.

* * *

September 10
Name the great golfer born this day, 1929. He won the US Open in 1960; was US Amateur Champion in 1954; won the British Open in 1961 and 1962; and the Masters in 1958, 1960, 1962, and 1964.

* * *

September 11
Name the controversial British writer born this day, 1885. He wrote *Lady Chatterley's Lover* and *Sons and Lovers*.

* * *

September 12
Who starred in TV's first 90-minute color spectacular seen this night, 1954?

* * *

September 13
Who was the famous military man born this day, 1860? He led the AEF during World War I.

* * *

September 14
Who was the pioneer birth-control advocate born this day, 1883?

* * *

September 15
Name the famous German movie star discovered in France this day, 1918. He starred in *Where the North Begins, The Night Cry, Jaws of Steel* and *The Frozen River*.

* * *

September 16
On this day, 1940, FDR signed the first peacetime law of its kind. What was it?

* * *

September 17
On this day, 1936, Chrysler Corporation began sponsorship of this radio show on CBS. The MC announced "The wheel of fortune goes 'round and 'round and where she stops nobody knows." Name the show.

* * *

238

September 18

In Stockholm, Sweden, this day, 1905, one of the most famous film actresses of all time was born. Her first movie was *Peter the Tramp;* her last was *Two-Faced Woman.* Name her.

* * *

September 19

On this day, 1930, Sir Thomas Lipton lost his fifth try at a trophy. What trophy is this?

* * *

September 20

This famous American writer was born this day, 1878. Author of *The Jungle* and the Lanny Budd series, he ran for Governor of California during the 30s on the EPIC ticket.

* * *

September 21

In 1866 on this day, the author of *The Time Machine* and *The Invisible Man* was born. Name him.

* * *

September 22

In 1961, on this day, a charming film comedienne died. She had appeared in *Little Old New York, Show People* and *Page Miss Glory.* Name her.

* * *

September 23

Montgomery Clift played this physician, who died this day, 1939. Name him.

* * *

September 24
Who made the first blind flight (with instruments only) this day, 1929?

* * *

September 25
Name the famed Mississippi author born this day, 1897. He won the Nobel Prize, and was also a Hollywood script writer (*To Have and Have Not; the Big Sleep; Land of the Pharoahs*).

* * *

September 26
Who was the gifted composer born this day, 1898? He wrote the scores for such shows as *Lady Be Good, Oh, Kay, Funny Face, Strike Up the Band, Girl Crazy,* and *Of Thee I Sing*.

* * *

September 27
Name the novelist and short story writer born this day, 1917. His books include *Rector of Justin* and *Portrait in Brownstone*.

* * *

September 28
What movie opened this day, 1934? It was based on the life of an English poetess who married a poet against her father's wishes.

* * *

September 29
Name the actress born this day, 1908. She won an Oscar in 1942 for *Mrs. Miniver*.

* * *

September 30
Who hit his 60th homer this day, 1927?

October 1

Name the pianist born this day, 1904. He retired in 1953, but returned to the concert stage in 1966.

*   *   *

October 2

On this day, 1938, Bob Feller struck out 18 men. What team was he pitching against?

*   *   *

October 3

Shirley MacLaine's first movie opened today, 1955. What is its name?

*   *   *

October 4

Chester Gould's famous comic strip debuted today, 1931. What is its name?

*   *   *

October 5

The father of rocketry was born this day, 1882. His name?

*   *   *

October 6

George Jessel turned down the lead in the movie that opened this day, 1927. What movie was it?

*   *   *

October 7

Who was the magnificent movie tenor who died this day, 1959?

*   *   *

October 8
From racing car driver to airline executive, with time out for war heroism, . . . this is the life of the man born this day, 1890. Name him.

* * *

October 9
Max Reinhardt's movie production of a Shakespeare play opened this day, 1935. Name it.

* * *

October 10.
Name the American actress born this day, 1900. Widow of playwright Charles MacArthur, a N.Y. theatre is named after her.

* * *

October 11
This Rodgers-Astaire film opened this day 1934. Music and lyrics by Cole Porter ("Night and Day" and "The Continental"). Name it.

* * *

October 12
The heroine of *"Call Me Madame"* was modeled after this hostess with the mostess, born this day, 1891. Name her.

* * *

October 13
All About Eve opened this day, 1950. Who directed this 7-Oscar film?

* * *

242

October 14

Who was the actor who died this day, 1959? He was born in Tasmania, and had panned for gold as a youth. His performance in *The Sun Also Rises* was painfully close to the truth, reflecting his own life.

*　*　*

October 15

The Great Dictator opened this day, 1940. Chaplin played Hynkel; who played Napaloni?

*　*　*

October 16

Name the great playwright born this day, 1888. Among other plays he wrote: *The Great God Brown* and *Marco Millions*.

*　*　*

October 17

Who is the actress born this day, 1905? She played Calamity Jane to Gary Cooper's Wild Bill Hickock in DeMille's *The Plainsman*.

*　*　*

October 18

Who was the American inventor who died at 84 this day, 1931: a) Steinmetz; b) Bell; or c) Edison?

*　*　*

October 19

Who was the actor who died this day, 1955? He played an American officer in *A Bell for Adano*.

*　*　*

October 20

Name the ball player born this day, 1931. In 1956 he won the following: AL Batting Championship; AL Runs Batted In; AL Home Run Champ; AL MVP.

* * *

October 21

Who were the two stars of *For Me and My Gal,* which opened this day, 1942?

* * *

October 22

The first broadcast from The *Graf Zeppelin* took place this day, 1933 on its route from South America to Miami. What was the *Graf Zepplin?*

* * *

October 23

The "Linit Bath Club Revue" debuted this day, 1932. Who made his radio debut on this show?

* * *

October 24

Name the American playwright born this day, 1904. He wrote the screenplay for *Gentleman's Agreement.*

* * *

October 25

There was a riot this day, when these items went on sale for the first time in 1939. What were they: a) nylon stockings; b) ball point pens; c) radial tires; or d) zippers?

* * *

October 26
Name the child actor (*The Kid*) born this day, 1914.

*   *   *

October 27
Who was the etiquette expert born this day, 1872?

*   *   *

October 28
Name the scientist born this day, 1914. His discovery helped eliminate an annual late summer scourge.

*   *   *

October 29
This movie, which opened this day, 1941, made Americans conscious of Wales and its special culture. What was its name?

*   *   *

October 30
What show was broadcast this day, 1938? Hint—an announcer told you "We are bringing you an eyewitness account of what's happening on the Wilmuth farm, Grovers Mill, New Jersey."

*   *   *

October 31
Name the actress born this day, 1912. With her husband, she appeared in *The Cowboy and the Senorita, Yellow Rose of Texas, Song of Nevada, San Fernando Valley, Lights of Old Santa Fe,* etc.

*   *   *

November 1
Name the author born this day, 1880. Among his novels: *The Nazarene, The Apostle,* and *Mary.*

*   *   *

November 2

The first a) newsreel theatre; b) drive-in bank; or c) miniature golf course opened this day, 1929.

*   *   *

November 3

What movie opened this day, 1939? Directed by Ernest Lubitsch, its screenplay was by Charles Brackett, Billy Wilder and Walter Reisch, and in supporting roles it had Sig Rumann, Felix Bressart and Alexander Granach as Russian emigres.

*   *   *

November 4

What well-known writer was born this day, 1906? With Frank Coniff and William Randolph Hearst, Jr., he interviewed Khruschchev in 1960.

*   *   *

November 5

Name the designer born this day, 1893. Among other innovations, he designed the "backwards-and-forwards" Studebaker.

*   *   *

November 6

Name the author born this day, 1921. He wrote *From Here to Eternity*.

*   *   *

November 7

Who was the actor who died this day, 1959? He played Gypo Nolan in *The Informer*.

*   *   *

November 8
Who was elected governor of California this day, 1966, after spending most of his working life in front of the movie cameras?

* * *

November 9
Name the movie actress born this day, 1913. Her first American movie was *Algiers,* and in *White Cargo* she appeared as Tondelayo.

* * *

November 10
Name the author born this day, 1893. He wrote the Mr. Moto stories for *The Saturday Evening Post.*

* * *

November 11
What happened in North Dakota this day, 1933?

* * *

November 12
Who was appointed Commissioner of Organized Baseball this day, 1920?

* * *

November 13
What car maker celebrated its twenty-third birthday this day, 1934, by assembling its tenth million car? a) Ford; b) Packard; or c) Chevrolet

* * *

November 14
What California community was incorporated this day, 1903?

* * *

November 15

Name the one-name conductor born this day, 1905. He is famous for his lush arrangements of standards.

November 16

Who was the movie actor who died this day, 1960? His first three sound movies: *The Painted Desert, The Easiest Way* and *Dance Fools Dance.*

*　　*　　*

November 17

Today, 1933, *The Invisible Man* opened. Who played him?

*　　*　　*

November 18

Who starred in *I Want To Live,* which opened this day, 1958?

*　　*　　*

November 19

Today, 1932, *I Am a Fugitive From a Chain Gang* opened. Who directed Paul Muni in this film?

*　　*　　*

November 20

Today, 1945, the trials of the German war criminals opened. In what German city did the trials take place?

*　　*　　*

November 21

Today, 1931, saw the opening of *Frankenstein.* Who wrote the original novel from which the movie was taken?

*　　*　　*

November 22

Name the Hoosier songwriter born this day, 1899. His most famous song: "Stardust."

* * *

November 23

On this day, 1934, *Imitation of Life* opened. Who wrote the original novel?

* * *

November 24

On this day, 1864, a French aristocrat who became an artist was born. Who directed the 1953 movie based on Toulouse-Lautrec's life?

* * *

November 25

Name the baseball great born on this day, 1914. His lifetime batting average is .325. He was AL Batting Champ in 1939 and 1940; led the AL in runs batted in in 1941 and 1948. He led the AL in home runs in 1937, and 1948. And he was AL MVP in 1939, 1941, and 1947.

* * *

November 26

Name the cartoonist born this day, 1922. His comic strip has done a lot for beagles.

* * *

November 27

Name the American dramatist who died this day, 1953. Blanche Sweet starred in the first version of a movie made from a play he wrote; Garbo in the second version.

* * *

November 28

Who took off for the South Pole this day, 1929: a) Byrd; b) Peary; or c) Freuchen?

* * *

November 29

Name the W.C. Fields comedy which opened this day, 1940. Fields wrote the screenplay under the pseudonym of Mahatma Kane Jeeves.

* * *

November 30

Name the movie actress born this day, 1920. Her movies include *The Adventures of Jack London, Up in Arms, The Princess and the Pirate, Wonder Man, The Best Years of our Lives, Captain Horatio Hornblower.*

* * *

December 1

Name the singer born this day, 1913. Songs which she made famous range from "My Heart Belongs to Daddy" to "I'm Going to Wash That Man Right Out of My Hair."

* * *

December 2

Name the actor who died this day, 1963. His films include *Elephant Boy, Cobra Woman, Hello, Elephant, Jaguar* and *A Tiger Walks.*

* * *

December 3

Who was the Polish author born this day, 1857? Movies made from his books include *Lord Jim.*

* * *

December 4

Who was the Broadway columnist who started his radio program this day, 1932? His two announcers were Richard Stark and Ben Grauer.

*   *   *

December 5

Name the actor-director born this day, 1906. He appeared in *Stalag 17* and *They Got Me Covered*. He directed *Laura* and *Exodus*, among other films.

*   *   *

December 6

This movie actor, born this day, 1870, was originally a Shakespearean actor, but became a hero of the silent Western. Name him.

*   *   *

December 7

Name the Viennese composer born this day, 1879. His filmed operettas include *The Firefly, Naughty Marietta* and *The Vagabond King*.

*   *   *

December 8

The first ship to enjoy this service (used this day, 1928) was the "SS Leviathan." It was: a) ship-to-shore phone; b) radar; or c) sonar.

*   *   *

December 9

On this day, 1902, "The Witch of the West" was born. Name her.

*   *   *

December 10
On this day, 1911, David Brinkley's former partner was born. Name him.

*   *   *

December 11
Name the New York City mayor born this day, 1882. During World War I he had been an Air Corps major, later a congressman.

*   *   *

December 12
Name the most important singer ever to have come out of Hoboken, born this day, 1917.

*   *   *

December 13
What was the name of the US gunboat sunk this day, 1937, by Japanese planes?

*   *   *

December 14
National Velvet opened this day, 1944. What horserace was the center of commotion in this flick?

*   *   *

December 15
On this day, 1896, the author of *A Tree Grows in Brooklyn* was born. What was her name?

*   *   *

December 16
Name the entertainer born this day, 1899. His films range from *Cavalcade* to *Brief Encounter*.

*   *   *

December 17

Name the author of *Tobacco Road,* born this day, 1903.

* * *

December 18

What Oriental immigrant was welcomed this day, 1936, in San Francisco?

* * *

December 19

Name the British actor born this day, 1902. His roles have included Buckingham in *Richard III,* Sir Edward Carson in *Oscar Wilde,* Micawber in *David Copperfield,* and the Caterpillar in *Alice's Adventures in Wonderland.*

* * *

December 20

Name the author who died this day, 1968. He wrote *Travels with Charlie, Of Mice and Men* and *Cannery Row.*

* * *

December 21

On this day, 1937, *Snow White and The Seven Dwarfs* opened. Name the Dwarfs.

* * *

December 22

On this day, 1937, The Lincoln Tunnel opened. Name the two states it connects.

* * *

December 23

On this day, 1907, Don McNeill was born. As MC of "The Breakfast Club," with whom did he "feud"?

* * *

253

December 24

On this day, 1905, the producer of *Two Arabian Knights* and *The Front Page* was born. Name him.

* * *

December 25

This was the "official" birthday (1899) of which socialite-turned-actor? He played a vampire in *The Return of Doctor X*.

* * *

December 26

In 1921 on this day, Steve Allen was born. Who is Steverino married to?

* * *

December 27

Today, 1917, saw the first issue of: a) *Colliers*, b) *Life*, or c) *Photoplay*.

* * *

December 28

Name the actor born this day, 1908. He was featured in *Holiday*, *Mississippi*, *State Fair*, *New Mexico*, *Johnny Belinda* and *Advise and Consent*, among other movies.

* * *

December 29

In the remake of *The Squaw Man* which opened this day, 1918, who had the original Dustin Farnum role?

* * *

December 30

Name the American politician born this day, 1873. He was defeated as Democratic candidate for President, 1928.

* * *

December 31
Name Garbo's last film, which opened this day, 1941.

*   *   *

ANSWERS

1.

1-f, 2-e, 3-a, 4-g, 5-b, 6-h, 7-d, 8-c, 9-j, 10-i

2.

1-d, 2-c, 3-h, 4-b, 5-a, 6-g, 7-f, 8-e

3.

1-k, 2-b, 3-h, 4-e, 5-j, 6-i, 7-d, 8-c, 9-g, 10-a, 11-f

4.

1. The National Youth Administration gave jobs to needy youths.
2. A girlie magazine of the 30s
3. Landing craft
4. Cigarets
5. Radio audience measurement services
6. The first ballpoint pens
7. FDR's private railroad car
8. Upton Sinclair
9. Sir James Chadwick
10. Dixie cups

5.

1-b, 2-a, 3-j, 4-i, 5-h, 6-g, 7-f, 8-e, 9-d, 10-c

The crossword grid reads:

R	E	D	S	H	O	E	S	S	A	C	R	E	D
O		U		E		D			D		E		I
S	O	M	E	R	S	E	T		M	O	T	H	E	R
S		B		O		N		G		U		E		E
E	R	O	T	I	C		M	E	L	B	L	A	N	C
N		S		N		B		N		L		R		T
			G	E	O	R	G	E	J	E	S	S	E	L
R		F			Y		R			E		E		Y
A	P	R	I	L	I	N	P	A	R	I	S		
T		E		I		N		L		R		S		L
H	U	C	K	S	T	E	R		R	E	S	C	U	E
B		K		T		R		A		L		R		N
O	I	L	M	E	N		S	N	E	A	K	E	R	S
N		E		N				N		N		E		E
E	L	D	E	S	T		P	A	R	D	O	N	E	D

6.

1-f, 2-g, 3-a, 4-h, 5-b, 6-i, 7-c, 8-e, 9-d, 10-j

7.

1-d, 2-e, 3-b, 4-a, 5-c

8.

1-d, 2-i, 3-e, 4-f, 5-h, 6-j, 7-g, 8-c, 9-a, 10-b

9.

1-b, 2-h, 3-c, 4-f, 5-b, 6-g, 7-i, 8-a, 9-d, 10-e

10.

1. Rough-House
2. Phyllis Blossom
3. Henry Tremblechin
4. Toots and Casper
5. Loweezy
6. He's a truant officer
7. In "Captain Easy"
8. Napoleon

257

9. Zero
10. Spooky
11. "Freckles and his Friends"

11.

1. Art Accord
2. Nick Adams
3. Ross Alexander
4. Pier Angeli
5. Fatty Arbuckle
6. Phillips Holmes
7. Karyn Kupcinet
8. Barbara La Marr
9. Carole Landis
10. Florence Lawrence

12.

1-d, 2-h, 3-c, 4-g, 5-b, 6-i, 7-a, 8-f, 9-j, 10-e

13.

1. He preceded J. Edgar Hoover as head of the Federal Bureau of Investigation (later the FBI).
2. Fletcher Henderson's.
3. Malcolm Campbell
4. Ernest Hemingway
5. Little Steel
6. a
7. Orson Welles. It was the lead-in to his broadcast, "The War of the Worlds."
8. John F. Kennedy
9. The founder of America First
10. Television

14.

1-m, 2-n, 3-l, 4-g, 5-k, 6-a, 7-j, 8-o, 9-i, 10-p, 11-h, 12-q, 13-a, 14-g, 15-f, 16-d, 17-e, 18-c, 19-b, 20-a

15.

1-i, 2-m, 3-o, 4-c, 5-g, 6-k, 7-b, 8-e, 9-j, 10-n, 11-a, 12-f, 13-l, 14-p, 15-h, 16-d

16.

1. Patricia Medina
2. Bette Davis
3. They all played Ma Barker.
4. They all played characters based on Bonnie Parker.
5. *Reap the Wild Wind*
6. Errol Flynn
7. Miklos Rozsa
8. She painted herself bronze for a role as an Egyptian girl in the 1923 *Ten Commandments,* and the makeup severely scarred her, forcing her to retire from the movies.
9. Fatty Arbuckle
10. Mollie Bird, head nurse

17.

1-c, 2-j, 3-f, 4-k, 5-g, 6-b, 7-i, 8-e, 9-a, 10-h, 11-d

18.

1-d, 2-e, 3-b, 4-g, 5-i, 6-f, 7-h, 8-a, 9-e, 10-c

19.

1. Sam Rice
2. Ann Pennington
3. William Jennings Bryan
4. Bernard Herrmann
5. Louis Armstrong
6. Anthony Asquith
7. Max Baer
8. Richard Barthelmess
9. Milt Britton
10. Eddie Peabody

20.

1-f, 2-g, 3-h, 4-i, 5-j, 6-a, 7-b, 8-e, 9-c, 10-d

21.

1-f, 2-h, 3-c, 4-e, 5-j, 6-a, 7-b, 8-g, 9-i, 10-d

22.

1. Sir Basil Zaharoff
2. They both played the role of McLeod in *Detective Story.* Bellamy created the stage role; Douglas played it in the William Wyler film.
3. Ma Barker and Machine Gun Kelly preferred the machine gun.
4. Vic Damone
5. Elliott Roosevelt's bull mastiff, who once got priority on a wartime flight and bumped three servicemen.
6. Albert Bassermann
7. John Barrymore and Michael Strange
8. Tallulah Bankhead
9. Cora Baird
10. Our Gang

23.

1-d, 2-f, 3-h, 4-j, 5-g, 6-i, 7-e, 8-c, 9-b, 10-a

Quiz-word No. 2

24.

1-f, 2-j, 3-a, 4-g, 5-k, 6-b, 7-h, 8-c, 9-i, 10-d, 11-e

25.

1-f, 2-a, 3-c, 4-h, 5-j, 6-e, 7-g, 8-b, 9-d, 10-i

26.

1. Bob Holloman of the St. Louis Browns, May 7, 1953
2. Len Koenecke, 1935
3. Al Lopez, 1,918
4. Hank Gowdy
5. Jack Graney holds all three records. His uniform number ing was sewn on the sleeve; numbering finally became official in 1929.
6. Ed Grant
7. Hank Greenberg
8. Harry Heilman
9. Gil Hodges
10. Danny Gardella

27.

1-d, 2-g, 3-i, 4-a, 5-l, 6-k, 7-b, 8-e, 9-d, 10-h, 11-j, 12-f

28.

1-g, 2-i, 3-j, 4-a, 5-h, 6-d, 7-c, 8-b, 9-f, 10-e

29.

1-j, 2-f, 3-c, 4-i, 5-e, 6-b, 7-h, 8-d, 9-a, 10-g

30.

1-a, 2-g, 3-a, 4-b, 5-d, 6-f, 7-e, 8-c, 9-c, 10-f

31.

1-d, 2-a, 3-g, 4-k, 5-j, 6-l, 7-i, 8-f, 9-c, 10-e, 11-h, 12-b

32.

   1. Science; he was Mr. Wizard.
   2. Irma Peterson, "My Friend Irma"
   3. June Taylor Dancers
   4. His daughter, Rosa, as a bride
   5. Jackie Gleason, in the "Honeymooners" segment
   6. A colonel
   7. Lulu McConnell
   8. Ben Casey
   9. "Queen For a Day" and "Truth or Consequences"
  10. Phil Silvers; Nat Hiken

33.

1-j, 2-d, 3-e, 4-c, 5-f, 6-i, 7-b, 8-h, 9-a, 10-g

34.

1-f, 2-a, 3-g, 4-b, 5-h, 6-c, 7-i, 8-d, 9-j, 10-e

35.

1-f, 2-a, 3-g, 4-h, 5-i, 6-j, 7-b, 8-c, 9-d, 10-e

36.

1-e, 2-f, 3-g, 4-h, 5-j, 6-i, 7-a, 8-b, 9-c, 10-d

37.

1-j, 2-i, 3-h, 4-g, 5-f, 6-a, 7-e, 8-d, 9-b, 10-c

38.

   1. Warner Baxter
   2. Rex Bell
   3. Charles Bickford
   4. Broncho Billy Anderson
   5. Elmo Lincoln
   6. Albert Dekker
   7. Dorothy Dandridge
   8. E. E. Clive

9. Michael Checkhof

10. Ruth Chatterton

39.

1. Richard Barthelmess

2. Mel Ferrer

3. Adolphe Menjou

4. Cesar Romero

5. Spencer Tracy

6. Will Rogers

7. Tyrone Power

8. Belle Bennett

40.

1. Marty Marion

2. Bill Terry

3. Rogers Hornsby

4. George Stallings

5. Leo Durocher

6. Connie Mack

7. Joe Cronin, 1934

8. Bucky Harris

Quiz-word No. 3

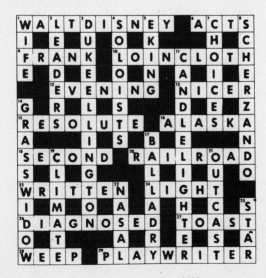

41.

1-e, 2-g, 3-f, 4-h, 5-a, 6-i, 7-b, 8-j, 9-c, 10-d

42.

1-d, 2-b, 3-f, 4-g, 5-a, 6-e, 7-h, 8-c

43.

1. Pancho Villa
2. Ivor Novello
3. Serge Voronoff
4. Tourist cabins
5. c
6. Charlie Dawes, later Vice President under Calvin Coolidge
7. a
8. "Deep Forest"
9. The Oldsmobile and the Reo was named for Ransom Eli Olds; Henry J. Kaiser had the Henry J. and the Kaiser-Frazer named for him.
10. "Old Creepy"

44.

1-h, 2-i, 3-j, 4-k, 5-f, 6-g, 7-e, 8-d, 9-c, 10-b, 11-a

45.

1-c, 2-h, 3-g, 4-e, 5-d, 6-a, 7-b, 8-f, 9-i, 10-j

46.

1-b, 2-a, 3-g, 4-f, 5-e, 6-j, 7-i, 8-h, 9-d, 10-c

47.

1. Jack Dempsey
2. Ezzard Charles, 1954
3. Primo Carnera, heavyweight
4. Billy Conn

5. First boxers to meet in three straight title bouts: June, 1959, June, 1960 and March, 1961
6. Archie Moore
7. Last heavyweight championship battle scheduled for 20 rounds
8. Jack Dempsey, July, 1923
10. McCarthy was a radio announcer; Tex Rickard was a promoter
11. Jack Johnson
12. Featherweight champ

48.

1-e, 2-d, 3-f, 4-c, 5-i, 6-j, 7-a, 8-b, 9-g, 10-h

49.

1-b, 2-d, 3-f, 4-g, 5-i, 6-h, 7-c, 8-e, 9-j, 10-a

50.

1. They're all members of the Mickey Mouse Club.
2. They were all movie buddies of Hopalong Cassidy.
3. They were all characters in *King Kong*.
4. They were all sunk at Pearl Harbor.
5. They all played Perry Mason.
6. They all had the role of Carol Clayton in *Saratoga*. Jean Harlow died while making the picture, Mary Dees replaced her and Paula Winslow dubbed in her voice.
7. They were all characters played by Humphrey Bogart (*Racket Busters*, *Dead End* and *Invisible Stripes*).
8. They're both named Captain America (Wyat appears in *Easy Rider*; Steve Rogers in comic books).
9. They both played the Cat Woman in "Batman".
10. They were all aliases of Ferdinand Waldo Demara, Jr., "The Great Imposter."

51.

1. Charles Bronson
2. Gala Poochie, Polka Dottie and El Squeako Mouse
3. Mickey Rooney
4. "Gunsmoke"
5. "Hazel"
6. Steve Allen
7. Captain Video
8. Walter Denton
9. Ollie; Oliver J. Dragon more formally
10. Lawrence Welk's

Quiz-word No. 4

52.

1. Joan Crawford; *Our Modern Maidens*
2. Richard Barthelmess
3. Elizabeth Bergner
4. *Mimi*
5. Rupert
6. Fairbanks played both brothers
7. Charles II
8. Betty Grable

53.

1-b, 2-c, 3-a, 4-d, 5-j, 6-h, 7-f, 8-e, 9-g, 10-i

54.

1. 24
2. Grover Cleveland Alexander, the only rightie mentioned
3. Philadelphia A's
4. Rogers Hornsby
5. Goose Goslin
6. The 1927 Yankees
7. Clarence Mitchell
8. Bill Wambsganss
9. The relief pitcher won 18, lost 1
10. He hit over .400 in a season: .407 in 1920, .420 in 1922

55.

1. Gladys Frazin
2. Claude Gillingwater
3. Carol Haney
4. Suzan Ball
5. Jenny Dolly
6. Weston and Winston Doty
7. Peg Entwhistle
8. Jack Fay
9. Eric Fleming
10. Margaret Campbell
11. Russ Columbo
12. Laird Cregar
13. Karl Dane
14. Bella Darvi

56.

1-b, 2-a, 3-c, 4-f, 5-d, 6-i, 7-g, 8-j, 9-h, 10-e

57.

1. The explosion of the "Hindenburg" in Lakehurst, N.J.
2. New Orleans
3. Bennett Cerf
4. Mary Jane Ward
5. Henry and Katherine Bellamann
6. Joseph C. Grew
7. Iwo Jima
8. The Japanese envoys negotiating with the United States on December 7, 1941
9. The Atlantic Charter; FDR and Winston Churchill
10. Major general

58.

1. Spring Byington
2. Bea Benaderet
3. Dwayne Hickman
4. Yvonne DeCarlo
5. Sally Field
6. Scott Forbes
7. Mark Richman
8. Jack Warden
9. Beverly Garland
10. Mike Connors

59.

1. They were each married to Clark Gable
2. Raymond Griffith
3. *Three Smart Girls*
4. Shirley Temple
5. *Castle on the Hudson*
6. *David Harum*
7. Pinto Ben
8. *Cimarron*
9. Bobs Watson
10. Joseph Cotten (Uncle Charlie)

60.

1-c, 2-f, 3-b, 4-a, 5-h, 6-g, 7-d, 8-e

61.

1. Early Wynn
2. Philadelphia Phillies
3. Walter Johnson pitched 113
4. 1937
5. The 1931 World Series; St. Louis Cardinals
6. Tommy Bridges
7. 1946
8. Fox hit the most homers in one season (58 in 1932); Hauser holds the record for lefties hitting the most for the A's (27 in 1924).
9. Ty Cobb
10. Virgil Trucks

62.

1-g, 2-j, 3-c, 4-f, 5-i, 6-b, 7-e, 8-h, 9-a, 10-d

Quiz-word No. 5

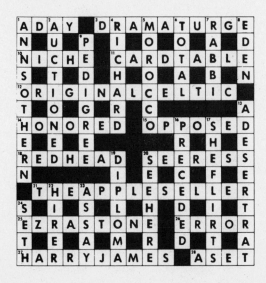

63.

1-c, 2-i, 3-e, 4-f, 5-j, 6-d, 7-h, 8-b, 9-g, 10-a

64.

1. The Empire State Building
2. Amelia Earhart
3. Billy Rose
4. The Sculptured Sundial
5. Democracity
6. The Pickwick and The Coconut Grove
7. Neville Chamberlain
8. Zane Grey
9. Al Smith
10. Edith Piaf

65.

1. c
2. Henderson
3. Mary Hartline
4. Steve Allen
5. All fight announcers
6. Cliff Robertson
7. Jack Carter
8. Wayne and Schuster
9. All bowlers
10. Tony Randall

66.

1. A. A. Milne
2. Aldous Huxley
3. Sinclair Lewis
4. F. Scott Fitzgerald
5. Ellen Glasgow
6. Irvin S. Cobb
7. Harold Bell Wright
8. Mary Roberts Rinehart

9. Gertrude Atherton
10. Sherwood Anderson

67.

1-f-VII, 2-h-II, 3-i-VIII, 4-e-IX, 5-g-I, 6-c-III, 7-j-VI, 8-a-V, 9-d-X, 10-b-IV

68.

1-d, 2-g, 3-c, 4-h, 5-a, 6-i, 7-f, 8-e, 9-b, 10-j

69.

1-i, 2-k, 3-d, 4-f, 5-g, 6-c, 7-l, 8-a, 9-h, 10-m, 11-j, 12-b, 13-e, 14-n

70.

1. Navy
2. Army
3. Army
4. Army
5. Navy
6. Navy Intelligence
7. Coast Guard
8. Air Force
9. WACs

71.

1-e, 2-a, 3-f, 4-b, 5-c, 6-g, 7-d

72.

1-c, 2-g, 3-b, 4-h, 5-a, 6-e, 7-j, 8-f, 9-i, 10-d

73.

1-h, 2-i, 3-d, 4-j, 5-k, 6-l, 7-c, 8-a, 9-g, 10-f, 11-e, 12-b

74.

1. Bing Crosby, in *She Loves Me Not*
2. Bill Kenny
3. "Christopher Columbus"
4. "Songs by Sinatra," "Songs for Sinatra," "The Frank Sinatra Show," and "Your Hit Parade"
5. The first group established by John Lennon (1955)
6. They were the Town Hall Quartet, on "The Fred Allen Show"
7. Judy Canova
8. Norman Brokenshire
9. Piano
10. Jesse Crawford

75.

1-d, 2-f, 3-g, 4-h, 5-i, 6-b, 7-j, 8-e, 9-c, 10-a

76.

1. *Anything Goes*
2. *Continental Varieties*
3. *Revenge With Music*

4. Horatio Hornblower
5. Peter Chambers and Peter Gunn
6. John Russell Coryell
7. Darling
8. Huey Long
9. c
10. Frigidaire refrigerators

77.

1-i, 2-h, 3-j, 4-a, 5-e, 6-g, 7-c, 8-f, 9-b, 10-d

78.

1-b, 2-d, 3-e, 4-f, 5-a, 6-c

79.

1. Sullivan
2. $64,000
3. Perry
4. Love
5. Bride
6. Talent
7. Bet
8. Skelton
9. My
10. Disney

80.

1-c, 2-f, 3-d, 4-g, 5-j, 6-e, 7-a, 8-i, 9-b, 10-h

81.

1-d, 2-f, 3-g, 4-j, 5-i, 6-c, 7-b, 8-a, 9-h, 10-e

82.

1. Lola Albright
2. Eve Arden

3. Linda Darnell
   4. Yvonne DeCarlo
   5. Rhonda Fleming
   6. Anne Francis
   7. Colleen Gray
   8. Dorothy Malone
   9. Vera Miles
  10. Barbara Nichols

83.

   1. A-1 Detective Agency ("I Love A Mystery")
   2. MGM
   3. Barry Goldwater's 1964 election slogan
   4. Boys Town
   5. "Don Winslow"
   6. "Green Lantern"
   7. Merrie Melodies
   8. "Red Ryder"
   9. Knute Rockne
  10. "Sam Spade"

84.

1-g, 2-h, 3-b, 4-e, 5-j, 6-m, 7-f, 8-c, 9-a, 10-d, 11-l, 12-k

85.

1-c, 2-g, 3-d, 4-j, 5-b, 6-f, 7-h, 8-i, 9-a, 10-e

86.

1-h, 2-a, 3-d, 4-g, 5-j, 6-c, 7-f, 8-i, 9-b, 10-e

87.

1-b, 2-e, 3-h, 4-c, 5-i, 6-j, 7-a, 8-d, 9-g, 10-f

88.

1-c, 2-a, 3-e, 4-b, 5-d

Quiz-word No. 7

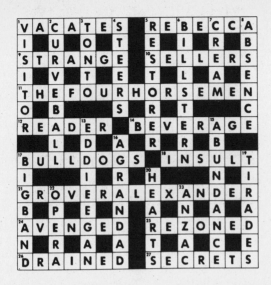

89.

1-d, 2-e, 3-h, 4-b, 5-i, 6-k, 7-a, 8-f, 9-j, 10-g, 11-c

90.

1. Martin Gable
2. John Cameron Swayze
3. William Frawley introduced "Mammy," before Al Jolson was associated with the song.
4. Little Jack Little
5. Musicologist Sigmund Spaeth
6. Fred and Adele Astaire broke up their brother-and-sister act in 1934, when Adele married Lord Charles Cavendish
7. President Harry S. Truman
8. FDR's press secretary
9. Gov. Strom Thurmond
10. Escaping from a southern chain gang. His story, "I Am a Fugitive From a Georgia Chain Gang," became the movie, *I Am A Fugitive From a Chain Gang.*

91.

1-d-II, 2-g-VIII, 3-e-VI, 4-h-VII, 5-b-III, 6-a-I, 7-c-IV, 8-f-V

92.

1-e-I, 2-f-II, 3-g-X, 4-h-VII, 5-i-VI, 6-j-III, 7-a-IX, 8-b-V, 9-c-IV, 10-d-VIII

93.

1-h-IX, 2-i-III, 3-g-X, 4-j-V, 5-d-VII, 6-b-IV, 7-a-XI (he was the commander before Kirk took over), 8-l-VIII, 9-k-XIV, 10-c-I, 11-e-XV, 12-m-XIII, 13-n-II, 14-a-VI, 15-f-XII

94.

1. Native Dancer
2. The 1906 Chicago White Sox. They won the American League pennant and the World Series with a team batting average of only .230.
3. The midget who pinchhit for the St. Louis Browns in one game in 1951.
4. "Pop" Warner
5. John Joseph Barry
6. The Chocolate Soldier
7. Hollywood Park
8. The New York Giants came out in the second half to score 27 points in the final quarter and overcame the Chicago Bear lead of 13-3.
9. The Pittsburgh Steelers and the Philadelphia Eagles combined teams in 1943.
10. They were part of the mighty 1944 St. Louis Browns—AL pennant winners.

95.

1-e, 2-b, 3-h, 4-d, 5-a, 6-g, 7-j, 8-f, 9-c, 10-i

96.

1-h-IV, 2-g-V, 3-f-VI, 4-i-VII, 5-c-I, 6-d-VIII, 7-j-IX, 8-e-III, 9-a-X, 10-b-II

97.

1. Gene Ahern
2. C. D. Russell
3. O. Soglow
4. Fontaine Fox
5. George McManus
6. Roy Crane
7. Lee Falk
8. Edwina Dunn

98.

1. Richard Rodgers
2. Lena the Hyena
3. The Dragon Lady
4. The Fantastic Four
5. a) William Graham Sumner; b) Stuart Chase
6. They were both imaginary landing places of Martians in *The War of the Worlds.* (New Jersey in Orson Welles' broadcast; Surrey, England, in the original novel by H. G. Wells.)
7. *Ziegfeld Follies of 1934*
8. F. Scott Fitzgerald
9. Luath, a bull terrier; Tao, a Siamese cat; and Bodger, a retriever
10. a

99.

1. Cream of Wheat; Cocomalt
2. Blackstone Cigars
3. Thrivo Dog Food
4. Mars Bars

5. International Sterling and 1847 Rogers Brothers
6. Willard Robinson
7. Bob Sweeney and Hal March
8. "Tillie the Toiler"
9. "Young Widder Brown"
10. Jack Benny's show

Quiz-word No. 8

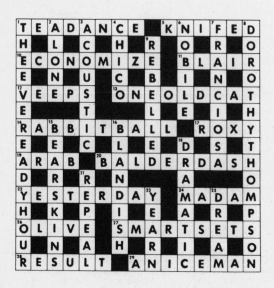

100.

1-d, 2-b, 3-g, 4-b, 5-c, 6-f, 7-a, 8-e

101.

1. Atticus Finch, Gregory Peck (*To Kill a Mockingbird*)
2. *Notorious*
3. Jules Dassin
4. Tom Mix
5. Flicka; The Pie
6. *Tortilla Flat*
7. *Peter and the Wolf*
8. Frank Sinatra
9. *Shane*

10. *The Cisco Kid*
11. *Ruggles of Red Gap*
12. *Movietone*

102.

1. Washington Redskins
2. d
3. Count Fleet
4. Nashua
5. b
6. Gertrude Ederle
7. Chicago Bears
8. Portsmouth Spartans
9. The introduction of the forward pass
10. Eddie Arcaro

103.

1. *The Man on the Flying Trapeze*
2. "It Had to Be You" and "As Time Goes By"
3. "Our Gang"
4. They both played Captain Bligh; Laughton in 1935; Howard in 1962.
5. General Lew Wallace
6. Ingrid Bergman
7. Mack Sennett
8. Latin
9. Pearl White
10. They each played Dr. Jekyll and Mr. Hyde

104.

1-c, 2-h, 3-d, 4-i, 5-e, 6-j, 7-a, 8-f, 9-b, 10-g

105.

1. Buick
2. Hudson

3. Dodge
4. Jordan Playboy
5. Studebaker
6. Packard
7. De Soto
8. Hudson

106.

1-f, 2-h, 3-d, 4-a, 5-b, 6-e, 7-g, 8-c

107.

1-f, 2-h, 3-j, 4-i, 5-g, 6-a, 7-b, 8-c, 9-d, 10-e

108.

1-c, 2-f, 3-d, 4-a, 5-e, 6-b

109.

1. Earle Sande
2. Lew Groza
3. Billy Sunday
4. Carl E. Stotz
5. Garnet Carter
6. Grantland Rice
7. Sam Riddle
8. Otto Graham
9. Lou Groza
10. Bo McMillin

110.

1-c, 2-f, 3-i, 4-b, 5-e, 6-h, 7-a, 8-d, 9-g, 10-j

111.

1-c, 2-d, 3-e, 4-a, 5-b

112.

1. A boundary set up to limit baseball team travel during the war years.
2. Calumet Farms
3. Herbert Hoover
4. a
5. Inventor of the autogiro
6. Another name for dimouts, named for Economic Mobilization czar James Byrnes.
7. Miniature editions of magazines for GI readers
8. A 10,000-ton Liberty Ship, launched 24 days after its keel was laid in 1942
9. They were all Axis broadcasters.
10. The first American warship to be torpedoed in our own waters

113.

1-g, 2-j, 3-c, 4-f, 5-i, 6-b, 7-e, 8-h, 9-a, 10-d

114.

1-g, 2-a, 3-c, 4-e, 5-i, 6-d, 7-j, 8-b, 9-f, 10-h

115.

1-g, 2-i, 3-j, 4-f, 5-h, 6-c, 7-d, 8-e, 9-a, 10-b

116.

1-g, 2-h, 3-a, 4-i, 5-b, 6-i, 7-c, 8-j, 9-d, 10-k, 11-e, 12-l, 13-f

117.

1-i, 2-j, 3-h, 4-k, 5-g, 6-l, 7-f, 8-m, 9-e, 10-n, 11-d, 12-o, 13-c, 14-p, 15-b, 16-p, 17-a, 18-q

118.

1-d, 2-g (Vincent Sherman completed the movie), 3-j, 4-c, 5-f, 6-i, 7-b, 8-e, 9-h, 10-a

119.

1. D.W. Griffith
2. Bobby Gregory
3. Mary Gordon
4. Helen Louise Gardner
5. Therese Thompson
6. Ian Fleming (*not* the author)
7. Hope Emerson
8. Frankie Bailey
9. Fay Bainter
10. Charles Coburn

120.

1. a
2. They were all Japanese war planes.
3. c
4. FDR's other dog
5. a) Flying Fortress, b) Digby, c) Liberator, d) Mitchell, e) Marauder
6. Lindbergh
7. The two-dollar bill
8. Cicero
9. The B-29 that dropped the A-bomb on Nagasaki
10. They were mob leader "Ma" Barker's boys.

121.

1-s, 2-g, 3-f, 4-e, 5-k, 6-a, 7-d, 8-l, 9-m, 10-n, 11-b, 12-c, 13-t, 14-o, 15-p, 16-h, 17-j, 18-q, 19-i, 20-r

122.

1. Lou Gehrig hit four homers consecutively, the first time in league history.
2. George Gibson
3. Glen Gorbous, August 1, 1957
4. Grover Cleveland Alexander

5. Luke Appling
6. Ernie Banks
7. Rex Barney
8. Moe Berg
9. Bobby Bragan
10. Ralph Branca
12. Duke Bresnahan
13. Bobby Brown

123.

1-h, 2-f, 3-d, 4-j, 5-c, 6-e, 7-b, 8-g, 9-a, 10-i

124.

1. Dorothy Lamour
2. Debbie Reynolds
3. Zsa Zsa Gabor
4. Porsche Spider
5. *Alias Nick Beal*
6. Anne Baxter
7. Brian Aherne
8. Ethel Barrymore
9. Gary Merrill
10. *Anchors Aweigh*

125.

1. Coach Cleats
2. Hudson High
3. Jefferson City Junior High
4. Jefferson High
5. Madison High
6. North Manual Trades High School
7. Riverdale High School

126.

1-b, 2-a, 3-a, 4-c, 5-b, 6-c, 7-b, 8-a, 9-b, 10-a

127.

1. Eddie Collins
2. Gene Conley; Boston
3. Chuck Connors
4. Dusty Cooke
5. Johnny Cooney
6. Clint "Scrap Iron" Courtney
7. Joe Cronin
8. Clyde ("Pea Ridge") Day
9. Al Demaree
10. Bill Dickey

128.

1-h, 2-a, 3-k, 4-d, 5-j, 6-i, 7-g, 8-f, 9-e, 10-c, 11-b

129.

1. *I'd Climb the Highest Mountain*
2. *State Fair*
3. David Wayne
4. *Twilight of Honor*
5. *The Jungle Princess*
6. Arsene Lupin
7. Fay Bainter
8. Anne Baxter
9. Lionel Atwill
10. They each played Judge Roy Bean

130.

1-c, 2-d, 3-a, 4-e, 5-h, 6-b, 7-j, 8-f, 9-g, 10-i

131.

1. a
2. a
3. They were all involved in the Teapot Dome scandal.
4. The 78-rpm record was discontinued.

5. Gary Powers in his U-2 plane
6. The trailer
7. a) the phone number of "Major Bowes Original Amateur Hour"; b) the phone number of the Pennsylvania Hotel, N.Y., and also the title of Glenn Miller's hit record
8. Pierce Arrow
9. Ken
10. Humphrey Bogart. His mother was a portrait painter who used her infant son as a model for the ad.

132.

1. Clouseau
2. Faraday
3. Gerard
4. Maigret
5. Miles Archer, Sam Spade's partner
6. *Hombre*
7. Erich Korngold
8. Elmer Bernstein
9. Sir William Walton
10. They were both actors who were also ministers.

133.

1-g, 2-h, 3-j, 4-i, 5-b, 6-e, 7-d, 8-c, 9-a, 10-f

134.

1. Dom DiMaggio
2. Larry Doby
3. Only 54 in 4 years
4. Bob Feller
5. Wes Ferrell, 38 homers
6. Johnny Frederick, six
7. Johnny Burnett (July 10, 1932, Cleveland vs. Phil.)
8. Sammy Byrd, who often pinch-ran for Ruth
9. Mickey Cochran
10. Jerry Coleman

135.

1. They were both Chevrolet dealers.
2. First nuclear-powered submarine
3. "Your Show of Shows"
4. a) tires; b) whitewall tires; c) lowering the roof; d) lowering the front end; e) driving around aimlessly
5. City Lights Bookshop. After the Chaplin film.
6. Dr. Alfred C. Kinsey
7. Robert Montgomery
8. LSD
9. Dwight D. Eisenhower's campaign train, 1952
10. Virtually wiped out during maneuvers at its Hiroshima base; the atomic bomb was dropped almost directly overhead

Quiz-word No. 9

136.

1-h, 2-i, 3-j, 4-d, 5-e, 6-c, 7-b, 8-g, 9-f, 10-a

137.

1. Edward G. Robinson
2. *King Creole*
3. Jets and Sharks
4. Lauren Bacall in *To Have and Have Not*
5. Raymond Burr
6. *Francis in The Haunted House*
7. Walter Huston
8. Noël Coward
9. Bullet
10. Ford Mustang

138.

1. President of General Motors
2. Grace Kelly
3. The bleep of Sputnik
4. St. Lawrence Seaway
5. Frisbees and Hula Hoops
6. The Old Man of *The Old Man and The Sea*
7. "I Like Ike!"
8. Richard Nixon
9. Flying saucers
10. Painting by the numbers

139.

1-f, 2-j, 3-e, 4-i, 5-d, 6-h, 7-b, 8-g, 9-c, 10-a

140.

1-e, 2-d, 3-g, 4-f, 5-c, 6-h, 7-i, 8-a, 9-b, 10-j

141.

1-c, 2-d, 3-e, 4-a, 5-j, 6-i, 7-h, 8-b, 9-g, 10-f

142.

1. Futurama
2. Queen Elizabeth, wife of George VI of England
3. *Becky Sharp*
4. To obtain the authority to close the banks for four days.
5. Henry Ford
6. Huey Long
7. d
8. a
9. Student League for Industrial Democracy, a radical student group
10. John L. Lewis

143.

1. Carmen: saxophone; Lebert: trumpet; Victor: saxophone
2. Rosalie and Sammy
3. Nan and Bert (8 years old); Flossie and Freddie (4 years old)
4. Connie, Vet and Martha
5. Dodge
6. Chevrolet
7. Duesenberg
8. Don and Phil
9. Fay and Evey
10. Charles Horace and William James
11. Christine, Dorothy and Phyllis

144.

1. The point system
2. Consumer groups that picketed stores over high prices
3. Demonstrations of soldiers still in Europe after World War II had ended
4. "Had enough?"
5. General Eisenhower
6. Canasta
7. Francis Parkinson Keyes

288

8. Mme. Elizabeth Shoumatoff
9. USSR
10. The Potsdam Declaration

Quiz-word No. 10

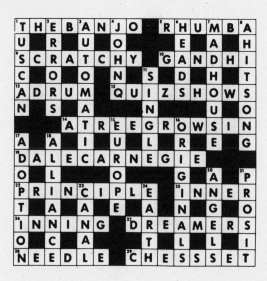

Semi-Official Nostalgia Diary: Answers

January 1.
The Man Who Came to Dinner

January 2.
Orphans of the Storm

January 3.
The March of Dimes

January 4.
"Myrt and Marge"

January 5.
FM radio

January 6.
Loretta Young

January 7.
Joseph Kennedy

January 8.
Charles de Gaulle

January 9.
Gypsy Rose Lee

January 10.
"The Flying Enterprise"

January 11
The Bitter Tea of General Yen

January 12.

She became the first elected woman Senator (Dem., Ark.)

January 13.

The Saar

January 14.

Franklin Delano Roosevelt and Winston S. Churchill

January 15.

Ignace Paderewski of Poland

January 16.

Carole Lombard

January 17.

Boston, Mass.

January 18.

Rudyard Kipling

January 19.

Howard Hughes

January 20.

In Old Arizona

January 21.

"Nautilus SS (N) 571"

January 22.

c

January 23.

Humphrey Bogart, *Casablanca, The Treasure of The Sierra Madre*

January 24.
First beer in cans sold this day

January 25.
John Dillinger

January 26.
Shephard's

January 27.
b

January 28.
The rope ski tow

January 29.
Victor Mature

January 30.
Franklin D. Roosevelt

January 31.
Zane Grey

February 1.
John Ford

February 2.
James Joyce

February 3.
They were the Four Chaplains

February 4.
Lake Placid, N.Y.

February 5.
To "pack" the Supreme Court by adding 6 new justices. The plan was defeated.

February 6.
City Lights.

February 7.
"Vox Pop"

February 8.
Boy Scouts of America

February 9.
The "Normandie"

February 10.
The singing telegram

February 11.
Farouk of Egypt

February 12.
Shanghai Express

February 13.
Kim Novak

February 14.
Dracula

February 15.
Mayor Anton Cermak

February 16.
Chester Morris

February 17.
Albert I of Belgium

February 18.
The planet Pluto

February 19.
Trail of the Lonesome Pine

February 20.
The first U.S. dog track was opened

February 21.
Battle of Verdun

February 22.
Robert Young

February 23.
Mt. Suribachi

February 24.
Manila

February 25.
Babe Ruth

February 26.
Jackie Gleason

February 27.
Elizabeth Taylor

February 28.
Milt Caniff

February 29.
   b

March 1.
   The Lindbergh child

March 2.
   King Kong

March 3.
   Jean Harlow

March 4.
   Herbert Hoover's

March 5.
   Rex Harrison

March 6.
   Lefty Grove

March 7.
   The Rhineland

March 8.
   Claire Trevor

March 9.
   Pancho Villa

March 10.
   Barry Fitzgerald

March 11.
   William Howard Taft

March 12.
Fireside Chats

March 13.
near Los Angeles

March 14.
Gilda

March 15.
My Little Chickadee

March 16.
The first liquid fuel-powered flight, ushering in the Age of Rocket Propulsion

March 17.
a

March 18.
Hawaii became the 50th state

March 19.
a

March 20.
Lauritz Melchior

March 21.
The Hatfield-McCoy feud

March 22.
Grand Coulee

March 23.
Amelia Earhart

March 24.
a

March 25.
a

March 26.
Popeye

March 27.
German forces were defeated on the Western front

March 28.
Eisenhower

March 29.
Pearl Bailey

March 30.
"American Town Meeting of the Air"

March 31.
Arthur Godfrey and Henry Morgan

April 1.
Frank Sinatra and Tommy Dorsey

April 2.
Sir Alec Guinness

April 3.
Doris Day

April 4.
The "Akron"

April 5.
Melvyn Douglas

April 6.
Anthony Eden

April 7.
Henry Ford

April 8.
b

April 9.
Paul Robeson

April 10.
John J. Anthony's "The Goodwill Hour"

April 11.
Jackie Robinson

April 12.
Grand Hotel

April 13.
a

April 14.
Texas City, Tex.

April 15.
Cary Grant

April 16.
"Fibber McGee and Molly"

April 17.
Brussels, Belgium

April 18.
a

April 19.
Took us off the gold standard

April 20.
''Your Hit Parade''

April 21.
Anthony Quinn

April 22.
The autogiro

April 23.
Shirley Temple

April 24.
The Easter Rebellion, Dublin, Ireland

April 25.
b

April 26.
b

April 27.
Rogers Hornsby

April 28.
Benito Mussolini

April 29.
b

April 30.
Eve Arden

May 1.
Kate Smith

May 2.
Bing Crosby

May 3.
Mary Astor

May 4.
Audrey Hepburn

May 5.
Alice Faye

May 6.
Seventh Heaven

May 7.
Anne Baxter

May 8.
Harry Truman

May 9.
Pancho Gonzalez

May 10.
Edison, the Man

May 11.
Salvador Dali

May 12.
Yogi Berra

May 13.
John Wayne

May 14.
a

May 15.
The Public Enemy

May 16.
Margaret Sullavan

May 17.
a

May 18.
TVA

May 19.
The Unholy Three

May 20.
James Stewart

May 21.
Humphrey Bogart and Lauren Bacall

May 22.
Laurence Olivier

May 23.

John D. Rockefeller

May 24.

First major league night game

May 25.

Gene Tunney

May 26.

Jimmie Rodgers

May 27.

Vincent Price

May 28.

Jim Thorpe

May 29.

Bonus March

May 30.

South Chicago

May 31.

Jersey City, N.J.

June 1.

c

June 2.

Queen Elizabeth II

June 3.

Lou Gehrig

June 4.
Mrs. Miniver

June 5.
The Marshall Plan

June 6.
To the first drive-in

June 7.
Dwight David Eisenhower

June 8.
Theodore Roosevelt

June 9.
Robert Cummings

June 10.
Lidice

June 11.
Jacques Yves-Cousteau

June 12.
Vic Damone

June 13.
Basil Rathbone

June 14.
to broadcast, over WEAR, Baltimore.

June 15.
Errol Garner

June 16.
Helen Traubel

June 17.
First round-world civil airline service

June 18.
Jeanette McDonald

June 19.
Guy Lombardo

June 20.
Lillian Hellman

June 21.
Tobruk

June 22.
Russia

June 23.
The Duke of Windsor, born the Prince of Wales, later became King Edward VIII.

June 24.
Stage Door Canteen

June 25.
Captains Courageous

June 26.
Pearl Buck

June 27.
Helen Keller

June 28.
Richard Rodgers

June 29.
Al Smith

June 30.
Gone With The Wind

July 1.
Easter Parade

July 2.
Sergeant York

July 3.
George Sanders

July 4.
Gina Lollabrigida

July 5.
NLRB (National Labor Relations Board)

July 6.
Hartford, Conn.

July 7.
China and Japan

July 8.
Vivien Leigh

July 9.
Samuel Eliot Morison

July 10.
It shrunk; smaller size bills were issued

July 11.
USAF Academy

July 12.
The Aga Khan

July 13.
W.C. Fields

July 14.
Howard Hughes

July 15.
Lebanon

July 16.
a

July 17.
Disneyland

July 18.
Wrong Way Corrigan

July 19.
Rome

July 20.
Adolf Hitler

July 21.
Ernest Hemingway

July 22.
John Dillinger

July 23.
Raymond Chandler

July 24.
Richard Nixon and Nikita Khrushchev

July 25.
"Andrea Doria" and "Stockholm"

July 26.
Fidel Castro

July 27.
Leo Durocher

July 28.
Empire State Building, New York City

July 29.
England

July 30.
Women Appointed (or Accepted) for Volunteer Emergency Service

July 31.
John F. Kennedy

August 1.
b

August 2.
Myrna Loy

August 3.
  The Cocoanuts

August 4.
  Sir Harry Lauder

August 5.
  Don Juan

August 6.
  The Good Earth

August 7.
  Rudolf Abel

August 8.
  Sylvia Sidney

August 9.
  Mohandas Gandhi

August 10.
  Rhonda Fleming

August 11.
  Herbert Hoover

August 12.
  Wings

August 13.
  WRNY telecast a 1^1/$_2$-square inch picture

August 14.
  U.S.

August 15.
    Will Rogers and Wiley Post

August 16.
    Bela Lugosi

August 17.
    Liberty Party

August 18.
    Ogden Nash

August 19.
    Orville Wright

August 20.
    Hallelujah

August 21.
    Trotsky

August 22.
    Dwight D. Eisenhower and Richard M. Nixon

August 23.
    Rudolf Valentino

August 24.
    Louis Lepke Buchalter

August 25.
    Abraham Lincoln

August 26.
    Gave women the vote

August 27.
    Color TV

August 28.
    Charles Boyer and Ingrid Bergman

August 29.
    Charlie Bird Parker

August 30.
    Raymond Massey

August 31.
    Ted Williams

September 1.
    Edgar Rice Burroughs

September 2.
    The Prisoner of Zenda

September 3.
    Kitty Carlisle

September 4.
    Underworld

September 5.
    Darryl Zanuck

September 6.
    Joan Crawford

September 7.
    Lex Barker

September 8.
"Morro Castle"

September 9.
So Proudly We Hail

September 10.
Arnold Palmer

September 11.
D. H. Lawrence

September 12.
Betty Hutton

September 13.
John J. Pershing

September 14.
Margaret Sanger

September 15.
Rin-Tin-Tin

September 16.
First peacetime draft law

September 17.
"Major Bowes and His Original Amateur Hour"

September 18.
Greta Garbo

September 19.
The America's Cup

September 20.
    Upton Sinclair

September 21.
    H. G. Wells

September 22.
    Marion Davies

September 23.
    Sigmund Freud

September 24.
    Jimmy Doolittle

September 25.
    William Faulkner

September 26.
    George Gershwin

September 27.
    Louis Auchincloss

September 28.
    The Barretts of Wimpole Street

September 29.
    Greer Garson

September 30.
    Babe Ruth

October 1.
    Vladimir Horowitz

October 2.
  Detroit Tigers

October 3.
  The Trouble With Harry

October 4.
  "Dick Tracy"

October 5.
  Robert H. Goddard

October 6.
  The Jazz Singer

October 7.
  Mario Lanza

October 8.
  Eddie Rickenbacker

October 9.
  Midsummer Night's Dream

October 10.
  Helen Hayes

October 11.
  The Gay Divorcee

October 12.
  Perle Mesta

October 13.
  Joseph L. Mankiewicz (also wrote the scenario)

October 14.
Errol Flynn

October 15.
Jack Oakie

October 16.
Eugene O'Neill

October 17.
Jean Arthur

October 18.
c

October 19.
John Hodiak

October 20.
Mickey Mantle

October 21.
Gene Kelly and Judy Garland

October 22.
A lighter-than-air craft

October 23.
Fred Allen

October 24.
Moss Hart

October 25.
a

October 26.
   Jackie Coogan

October 27.
   Emily Post

October 28.
   Dr. Jonas Salk

October 29.
   How Green Was My Valley

October 30.
   The War of the Worlds

October 31.
   Dale Evans

November 1.
   Sholem Asch

November 2.
   a

November 3.
   Ninotchka

November 4.
   Bob Considine

November 5.
   Raymond Loewy

November 6.
   James Jones

November 7.

Victor McLaglen

November 8.

Ronald Reagan

November 9.

Hedy Lamarr

November 10.

J. P. Marquand

November 11.

First great dust storm of the 30s

November 12.

Kenesaw Mountain Landis

November 13.

c

November 14.

Hollywood

November 16.

Clark Gable

November 17.

Claude Rains

November 18.

Susan Hayward (she won an Oscar)

November 19.

Mervyn LeRoy

November 20.
Nuremberg

November 21.
Mary Shelley

November 22.
Hoagy Carmichael

November 23.
Fannie Hurst

November 24.
John Huston

November 25.
Joe DiMaggio

November 26.
Charles Schulz

November 27.
Eugene O'Neill

November 28.
a

November 29.
The Bank Dick

November 30.
Virginia Mayo

December 1.
Mary Martin

December 2.
Sabu

December 3.
Joseph Conrad

December 4.
Walter Winchell

December 5.
Otto Preminger

December 6.
William S. Hart

December 7.
Rudolf Friml

December 8.
a

December 9.
Margaret Hamilton

December 10.
Chet Huntley

December 11.
Fiorello LaGuardia

December 12.
Frank Sinatra

December 13.
''Panay''

December 14.
The Grand National

December 15.
Betty Smith

December 16.
Noel Coward

December 17.
Erskine Caldwell

December 18.
The first giant panda was admitted to the San Francisco Zoo

December 19.
Ralph Richardson

December 20.
John Steinbeck

December 21.
Doc, Bashful, Grumpy, Sleepy, Sneezy, Happy and Dopey

December 22.
New York and New Jersey

December 23.
Tom Breneman of "Breakfast in Hollywood"

December 24.
Howard Hughes

December 25.
Humphrey Bogart

December 26.

Jayne Meadows

December 27.

c

December 28.

Lew Ayers

December 29.

Elliott Dexter. Warner Baxter had the role in the 1931 tal remake.

December 30.

Alfred E. Smith

December 31.

Two-Faced Woman